Stop Eating Your

EMOTIONS

Stop Eating Your EMOTIONS

How to Live Healthy and Eat Happy

Isabelle Huot
Catherine Senécal

Foreword by Sophie Grégoire Trudeau

 Collins

Stop Eating Your Emotions
Published originally under the title *Cessez de manger vos émotions* © 2017,
Editions de l'Homme, division of Groupe Sogides Inc.
(Montreal, Quebec, Canada)

English-language translation © 2018, Editions de l'Homme, division of
Groupe Sogides Inc. (Montreal, Quebec, Canada)
All rights reserved

Published by Collins, an imprint of HarperCollins Publishers Ltd,
by arrangement with Groupe Sogides Inc., Montreal, Quebec, Canada

This book contains advice and information relating to healthcare. It should be used to supplement rather than replace the advice of your doctor or another trained health professional. If you know or suspect you have a health problem, it is recommended that you seek your physician's advice before embarking on any medical program or treatment. All efforts have been made to ensure the accuracy of the information contained in this book as of the date of publication. This publisher and the authors disclaim liability for any medical outcomes that may occur as a result of applying the methods suggested in this book.

Diagnostic criteria for binge eating disorder reprinted with permission from the *Diagnostic and Statistical Manual of Mental Disorders*, fifth edition, (Copyright © 2013). American Psychiatric Association. All rights reserved.

HarperCollins books may be purchased for educational, business, or sales promotional use through our Special Markets Department.

HarperCollins Publishers Ltd
Bay Adelaide Centre, East Tower
22 Adelaide Street West, 41st Floor
Toronto, Ontario, Canada
M5H 4E3

www.harpercollins.ca

Library and Archives Canada Cataloguing in Publication
information is available upon request.

ISBN 978-1-4434-5735-4

Printed and bound in the United States
LSC/C 10 9 8 7 6 5 4 3 2 1

CONTENTS

Foreword by Sophie Grégoire Trudeau

Tell me what you eat, I'll tell you who you are.
—Jean Anthelme Brillat-Savarin

Imagine that you're alone: no one is looking at you; you're having a quiet moment in the car, at home, outdoors—wherever you are. How are you treating yourself? What kind of conversation are you having with yourself? Are you being generous, gentle, encouraging, and optimistic? Or have you been comparing yourself to others and always finding yourself inadequate, undervaluing yourself, and not really taking care of yourself? Whatever your background, your difficulties, and your personal journey, there's still plenty of time to learn to love yourself and respect yourself. Better late than never.

Just like physical activity and well-balanced sleep, diet is a major part of a healthy lifestyle and well-informed self-care. There are many foods we can easily find that nourish our brain, support our immune system, and help regulate our hormones and our sleep. This book teaches you simple ways to improve your health, your quality of life, and your longevity. Once we begin to eat better and exercise, the rest follows, too. We're energized, positive, and better prepared to overcome life's obstacles, large and small.

Taking care of ourselves is the best gift of all. Let's be honest with ourselves, respectful toward ourselves, and give our bodies the very best. Let's make sure our children have nutritional knowledge that will serve them well throughout their lives. Let's use what Mother Nature offers us to help shape the well-being of our generation and those to come.

Healthy eating isn't rocket science—with your body, heart, and mind you can change the world!

To your health and the health of all your loved ones!

—Sophie

PREFACE

A word from Isabelle

I've always been interested in eating behaviour disorders. I studied psychology first and then went into nutrition, wanting to help people in a holistic way. Later, I did my internships in anorexia-bulimia both at Centre hospitalier universitaire Sainte-Justine in Montreal and CHU in Geneva, where I completed part of my studies. When I started my clinical practice 25 years ago, my childhood friend Nancy, a member of Overeaters Anonymous, referred many people to me, all suffering from compulsive eating. This became my specialty. Seeing my clients feel better by improving their relationship with food, changing their body image, and regaining pleasure in eating makes me happy! Compulsive eating is a complex disorder, and I soon understood that having a psychologist at Kilo Solution would guarantee greater long-term success. So I approached Catherine, the founder of the CHANGE psychology clinics, to work alongside my team of nutritionists. For years, we have collaborated to provide support to people in difficulty and help them on their journey toward healing. This book would not have been the same without the crucial psychological input Catherine and her writing have supplied. I hope with all my heart that our advice will help you make peace with food and your body.

A word from Catherine

Before I had even turned 20, while I was doing my BA in psychology, I began to volunteer by facilitating groups for Anorexia and Bulimia Quebec (ANEB). For me, treating eating disorders was a passion right from the start. I discovered a group of people I cared about whose problems presented challenges that few professionals specialized in. Later, for my doctorate in psychology, I wrote my dissertation on detecting eating disorders in children, and I did my internships with adults in the Eating Disorders Program at the Douglas Mental Health University Institute and the Royal Victoria Hospital. After founding the CHANGE clinics, I realized just how few specialized services were available to people with binge eating disorder. When Isabelle approached me several years ago, I discovered a professional and diligent nutritionist who makes sure her team detects eating disorders. Isabelle has shown unflagging confidence in my team and me, and our collaboration, based on a passion for treating eating disorders, gave rise to this book. I encourage you to take the time to do the exercises we've included. Pausing to take care of ourselves is the best gift we can give ourselves. I sincerely hope this will lead you ever closer to your happiness and well-being.

CHAPTER
1

A LOVE-HATE
RELATIONSHIP
WITH FOOD

You've controlled yourself today: fruit yogurt for breakfast, a salad at noon . . . until the time comes to leave work. You feel like eating something, and you struggle not to stop at the corner store on the way home. In the end you manage to make it through your front door, telling yourself you can hold on. Once you're in the kitchen, though, you can't control yourself any longer. You take out crackers first, then cheese—and then on it goes. Too bad. But tomorrow you'll get a hold of yourself and start from square one. Again . . .

Or maybe you're the type who eats normally at supper with your children or your partner, but then in the evening, when the house quiets down, certain thoughts start buzzing at you nonstop like an irritating insect. The urge for chocolate or chips, for example. You know they're bad for your weight or your health, but you can't control the impulses . . .

Do these scenarios sound familiar? Do you recognize yourself in them? You're not alone, you know. Many people have a love-hate relationship with food that monopolizes their thoughts and considerably affects their quality of life.

Developing a healthy relationship with food isn't easy in a society where food is often identified as good or bad, restrictive diets are more popular than ever, and value is placed on thinness. Yet sometimes we just need a few tools to improve our relationship with food and begin to eat naturally again, guilt-free. If the problem is more serious and an eating behaviour disorder is diagnosed, the road ahead will be longer, and you'll no doubt need help from experts or a support group. We'll come back to this topic a little later on.

First, let's pinpoint the problem

Is there *anyone* who has never eaten a whole bag of chips or cookies? Is scarfing down the whole bag the sign of an eating behaviour disorder? Not necessarily, since all of us sometimes eat when we're not hungry. But when we lose control frequently, over and over again, when these episodes are linked to specific emotions and interfere with our physical or mental health, then we need help.

A typical example . . .

Manon has been on various diets in her life. Her weight regularly fluctuates about 30 pounds. She's tried every diet: powdered protein, laxatives, food combining, cabbage soup, the grape cure . . . Yet she's never managed to maintain her weight loss. Highly emotional and private, Manon never wants to let her family or her boss down. She's always given a lot to other people and at 45, she'd like to think a little more about herself and improve her own health. She came to see us to learn how to eat in a healthy way again, especially how to better manage her emotions, which cause her to lose control several times a week. Food is so comforting after a tough day . . .

Manon's case isn't unique; it's actually common. What strategies will be effective in guiding her toward a stable weight and an improved relationship with food? This book explores several approaches to point Manon—and you, dear reader—in the right direction.

Kinds of loss of control

Overeating
"When I lose control, I eat desserts and a big bag of chips fast. I feel like I can't stop, and I feel guilty afterward. I hate my body when I've eaten compulsively."

Emotional eating
"Sometimes, when I'm stressed, I go to the corner café and buy two pastries, when instead I could do a breathing exercise to calm myself down. I don't feel guilty for having eaten them, but I worry about the effects on my weight and my health, and I'd like to manage my emotions differently."

Epicureanism*
"I eat too much when someone cooks a gourmet dinner. This happens from time to time on special occasions, and cooking and enjoying food together is such a pleasure."

---

* The epicurean does not have an unhealthy relationship with food. Eating too much at a festive gourmet dinner is common and nothing to worry about.

What exactly is binge eating?

The term *binge eating* will be used throughout this book to describe those moments of loss of control when you eat without really feeling hungry, more than you would have liked, and with a feeling of guilt. The loss of control may be occasional or recurrent.

Does everyone eat the same thing during a binge eating episode?

Binge eating varies from person to person. For some, it may mean eating a whole bag of chips. For others, the bag of chips will be followed by a quart of ice cream and half a bag of store-bought cookies. Loss of control often involves foods that are "forbidden" (by diets, for example). Usually, this means chips, chocolate, ice cream, cereals, cookies, etc. Sweet foods with a high fat content are the most likely to be eaten during binge eating attacks.[1]

What can trigger binge eating?

A number of key factors can explain why we give in to binge eating at certain times:

1. **Negative emotions (anger, loneliness, boredom, anxiety, etc.) and stress.**[2]
    Emotions that are hard to manage can make us want to suppress them, and food can be effective for this purpose. Episodes of binge eating sometimes give people a "break" from powerful emotions they feel they can't control. This eating behaviour thus becomes a lifeline for people so they can "survive" psychologically.

2. **The restrictions we impose on ourselves, whether mental (not allowing ourselves to eat certain categories of foods) or caloric (not allowing ourselves to eat enough food).**
   You know this story—we've all heard it a thousand times. About the people who go on a diet, lose weight, then gain back more than they lost and blame themselves: "It's my fault—I just love to eat so much—I can't control it."

   Our clients often describe themselves as people who can't stop eating, who have no willpower. But any one of us, if we placed unrealistic demands on ourselves like losing 5 to 10 pounds a week or not eating any of our favourite foods, would wind up giving in and feeling unable to cope.

   Caloric restriction (not eating enough), or mental restriction (not allowing ourselves to eat certain foods), can produce the same failed result.

Cycle of binge eating

Restriction

Obsession

Binge
eating

This is why quick-weight-loss diets don't work. Caloric and mental restriction triggers binge eating, which acts to ensure the body's "survival" when it fears being deprived of food. Since your body is unaware that you yourself are imposing the restriction, it tries to protect you from the coming famine and stockpiles a few pounds as a preventive measure. If, after an episode of binge eating, you compensate by restricting your diet even more, the obsession recurs and the cycle continues.

True or false?

Eating very little makes you lose weight.

False

On the contrary. Metabolism slows down considerably in people who eat too little, hindering weight loss.

Depriving yourself leads to ... eating more!

Did you know that people who restrict what they eat end up eating more than those who eat normally?[3] One study was able to demonstrate this.

Two groups of participants were recruited, allegedly to take part in a taste test. The first group consisted of people who ate normally. The second group consisted of people who regularly went on weight-loss diets. In both groups, some participants were asked to consume one or two milkshakes and some participants not to drink any at all. Afterward, all the participants were encouraged to eat as much ice cream as they wanted.

In the group of people who ate normally, those participants who had consumed one or two milkshakes ate *less* ice cream, since they listened to their fullness cues. In the group of people who were regularly on a diet, those participants who had had a milkshake or two ate *more* ice cream. Since these participants had already consumed a "forbidden" food, they appeared to have said to themselves, "The day is ruined anyway, so I might as well take advantage of it . . ."

How about you? Do you, too, believe your day is ruined if you cave in and eat something less nutritious?

Inherent in following a diet is the idea of good or bad, of mental restriction, which makes us eat more when we break our food rules—unlike people who don't have rules and use their hunger as a guide for feeding themselves. "All or nothing" thinking is a syndrome we often see in our clients. As soon as clients with an eating disorder or an unhealthy relationship with food eat something they consider "bad," they view the day as ruined and go off the rails.

For example, you give in to a chocolate croissant at a morning office meeting and then you say to yourself, "That's it, my day is shot. While I'm at it, I may as well keep on eating badly today and start again fresh tomorrow." And if it's Thursday, you may as well wait until Monday, which is a better day to start a diet again, right?

To break this vicious cycle, it's important to aim for moderation and to include all foods—in particular, to change your thinking so you eliminate the guilt associated with consuming a food or a meal you consider less than perfect. We'll come back to this in later chapters.

3. **Feeling fat or bloated, which can lead to difficulty with self-care, a sense of failure, or sabotage.**
Many people weigh themselves daily and let the scale determine their mood for the rest of the day. This is another perfect example of the "all or nothing" thinking we've already referred to. With this thinking, when you weigh yourself and the scale reads lower, the day will be good, since you've succeeded. But if the number on the scale is up the next day, the day is a failure, ruined, and

you feel weak and lacking in willpower. This logic gives a lot of power to what is just a number, doesn't it?

Yet, importantly, several factors can influence the number on the scale. When you weigh yourself every day, wide fluctuations are common—although it's physiologically impossible to lose or gain three pounds in one day! In fact, to gain a pound, you have to take in an extra 3,500 calories. So, to gain three pounds in one day you'd have to consume 10,500 extra calories. Impossible, right? What you measure by weighing yourself frequently is simply water retention. Have you eaten salty foods? Exercised? Had a lot of fibre? Hormonal fluctuations can also explain a daily weight gain that bears no relationship whatsoever to increased body fat.

The graph below shows the weight changes of someone on a normal diet.

Weight change over 6 weeks on a normal diet

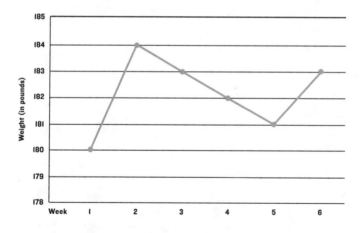

This graph shows a weight that varies between 180 and 184 pounds. It's easy to imagine the anxiety someone might feel if weighed on days when their weight is at the upper limit.

Weight goes up a little and down a little every week, like small waves. What's important is to stand back far enough to see that these waves make the same small movements independent of external factors.

Natural weight vs. healthy weight

People often talk about a *healthy weight*, a standard that has to be reached for good health. But we seldom hear people talking about *natural weight*, or *set point*,[4] which is based on the theory that each of us has a genetically determined weight. Like a bottle cork floating on water, the body determines its homeostatic weight, the point at which all its components are able to work as efficiently as possible. Our genetic heritage would therefore seem to determine how much we weigh. For example, if our parents have been obese all their lives, it's very likely that our natural weight is higher than our healthy weight. On the other hand, if our parents have a lower natural weight, it's very likely our natural weight will also be lower.

The only way to raise your set-point weight is to force yourself to alternate periods of restrictive dieting with periods of weight gain. In response to dietary restriction, the body protects its reserves and lets the brain know that it needs fatty and sweet foods immediately to "survive."

It's also important to distinguish between "being full" and putting on weight. For example, if you eat a large plateful of pasta for supper, each gram of carbohydrate will be stored with three grams of water in your reserves, which will make the needle on the scale rise temporarily. But does that mean you've gained weight?

If we followed that logic, it would mean that when you have a bowel movement and the weight on the scale drops, you're thinner. This really does not make sense, since being full does not mean being fatter. It doesn't translate into an automatic weight gain because fullness is a perception, a feeling. We mustn't let the needle on the scale affect our mood; weight varies too much naturally.

True or false?

It's good to weigh yourself every day.

False

A daily or even weekly weigh-in perpetuates an obsession with your body and food. One weigh-in a month is enough. The ideal is to allow yourself a range of five pounds. As soon as you go over the upper limit, make a few changes, like choosing smaller portions and getting more exercise.

A weigh-in can be a useful tool only when it's used in the long term. Weighing yourself once a month is enough to see a real difference in your weight. You can even get rid of your scale if it causes too much anxiety! Weighing yourself only in the presence of an expert (nutritionist, psychologist, kinesiologist) is also a good idea. They can explain the number on the scale and help you manage emotions associated with the results.

Binge eating disorder: when compulsive eating runs our lives

Instead of simply eating too much all the time, people with binge eating disorder experience episodes of compulsive eating during which they quickly ingest large amounts of food. People afflicted experience a loss of control during these episodes, followed by a feeling of enormous guilt and shame. This is the beginning of a vicious cycle. The more distressed they feel about their binges, the more frequently the behaviour seems to occur. Because they do not use inappropriate compensatory behaviours (vomiting, use of laxatives, etc.) the way people with bulimia do, many binge eaters are overweight or obese.

Rarely have we come across a group of people as unhappy as binge eaters. And yet, this disorder remains little recognized. The term *overeater* is also often used. Struggling daily against the one extra mouthful that triggers a cascade of compulsive eating, overeaters live in a state of profound turmoil. Every meal or snack is a challenge to their self-control and their ability to tune in to physical sensations of hunger. The inevitable feeling of guilt that follows every time they lose control is destructive. Low self-esteem, anxiety, and shame lead to psychological distress.

Binge eaters focus on their bodies; since these have been subjected to much abuse, this focus only reinforces weak self-esteem. Beginning drastic diets over and over again simply reinforces the compulsive-eating problem, resulting in another failure, a weight subject to the yo-yo effect, and harmful guilt.

A few important facts about binge eating disorder

In contrast to bulimia (see appendix I for the difference between binge eating and bulimia), which is much more common in women, nearly 40 percent of binge eaters are men. Although no exact statistic is available, it's estimated that 9 percent of the population suffers from this disorder, whereas bulimia affects just I to 2 percent.

Binge eating disorder:
- Is widespread among people of all ethnic origins.
- Is more common in people who are trying to lose weight.
- The average age of people affected is 40 to 50.

Other eating behaviour disorders (anorexia, bulimia, night-eating syndrome, etc.) are discussed in appendix I.

Do I have a problematic relationship with food?

In spite of the points discussed so far, you might still be confused about your relationship with food. This screening questionnaire[5] will help you:

	YES	NO
Do I feel like I'm losing control when I eat?	☐	☐
Am I constantly thinking about food?	☐	☐
Do I feel like eating even when I don't have hunger cues?	☐	☐
Are specific locations or hiding places reserved for unhealthy foods?	☐	☐
Are some foods eaten in "secret"?	☐	☐
Do I keep eating even when I feel too full?	☐	☐
Is the consumption of some foods exacerbated by emotions like stress, worry, or unhappiness?	☐	☐
Do I have a feeling of disgust, shame, or depression after meals?	☐	☐
Is the feeling of powerlessness greater than the desire to stop eating?	☐	☐

	YES	NO
Do I feel generally unsatisfied, no matter how much food I've eaten?	☐	☐
Do you binge at least once a week?	☐	☐
Over time, have these binges resulted in weight gain or obesity?	☐	☐

Analysis of the responses

Between one and three positive responses: You should keep an eye on your diet in the coming months and consider seeing a specialist. Your relationship with food might sometimes be conflicted.

Four or five positive responses: You should make an appointment with a specialist to discuss these risky behaviours. It may also be helpful to talk about your food habits with a close friend or family member.

Six or more positive responses: You should make an appointment with a specialist to evaluate the binge eating symptoms highlighted by this questionnaire.

If you need to seek help, even as a preventive measure, giving the results of the questionnaire to your healthcare professional will be beneficial. This will show that you have a good understanding of the situation and will help you answer supplementary questions from the doctor, nutritionist, or psychologist.

If you feel unhappy about frequent compulsive eating or you think you may be suffering from binge eating disorder, the second part of this book will be a useful aid to help you on your journey. To start right away, go to chapter 8.

In every case, the recommendations and exercises suggested in this book will help you get your health back on track. Chapter by chapter, you'll learn not only dietary strategies to better control your cravings and appetite, but also cognitive strategies to rethink your relationship with food and better manage your emotions.

> *"To win the love and admiration of others, I constructed my personality as a function of what they expected of me. Instead of searching for the true meaning of my being, by listening to the real being crying out inside me, I smothered it with too much food. I really do mean an excess of food, not just my regular meals. And despite my efforts to control myself, there'd always be jokers who'd come up to me and say, 'Oh come on, Ginette, you've got to eat something!'*
>
> *We have to remember that habits are living things. It's painful and hard to change. It will always be easier to stay with what we know than to head into the unknown. It feels safer and causes less fear. In my life, I've discovered that there's something abnormal, something that kills me, obsesses me constantly, and is*

definitely stronger than I am: food . . . goddamn food!

All my life I've told myself that my excess weight was the only thing standing in the way of my happiness and that by losing it, I could get closer to people more easily. It seemed to me I would have been less emotionally dependent, I would have felt less guilty, I would have been less fearful, I would have been less shy, less critical, and I wouldn't have cultivated so much resentment. I would have been a lot less jealous and possessive. It also seems that when we're fat, we're dishonest, too.

It's as if I forgot all the times I tried to lose weight, all the methods I used to get there—and believe me, there were many: with the help of a naturopath; in the hospital for a sleep cure; through hypnosis; with a sexologist and a psychologist; in psychoanalysis; with amphetamines and diuretics; by following the diets of doctors Colpron, Atkins, and Martineau; by getting injections; by going on an extreme physical exercise program. I also counted my calories, my carbohydrates; I swallowed supplements, vitamins, etc. How was it possible I was able to follow all these diets? And then one day, at one point in time, I had the perfect body: 36–26–36 (in inches) . . . Ah, how beautiful I was! But nothing had changed except my body. Inside, I was still just as unhappy. And each time I lost weight it came back as fast as it had gone. Why? . . . Why?

Even today, there are men and women who remember how beautiful I was and tell me so with a kindness that kills me every time: 'You were so beautiful, Madame Reno. What happened?' Some men have admitted to me that they desired me back then. What happened to me? It's not funny. Along with success came anxiety, the fear that people would discover who I truly was, because deep down I believed I was nothing. And yet people envied me . . . To hide all this suffering, I wore masks; I had a constant fear of ending up all alone in my life, with no one to share it.

Eating destructively is just as dangerous as abusing alcohol or drugs. I now know it's a serious disease, and I know that each day you can get better, but not on your own!"

—Ginette Reno, OC CQ CAL

(Officer of Canada; Chevalier du Québec; Chevalier de l'ordre des Arts et des Lettres, France)

Remember

✓ Many factors influence our relationship with food. Losing control from time to time by eating beyond the point of fullness is no cause for alarm. It happens to us all.

✓ If we lose control repeatedly every week or we're preoccupied with our diet, it's important to take care of ourselves and get help.

✓ The difficulty of managing strong emotions, imposing food prohibitions on ourselves, and placing too much importance on our weight can lead to compulsive eating.

✓ Our weight varies naturally depending on several factors.

✓ When we stand back and observe ourselves without being judgmental, we are able to understand the dynamics of our relationship with food and with our bodies.

CHAPTER

ADAPTING YOUR DIET TO BETTER MANAGE BINGE EATING

Now that you have a better understanding of what triggers binge eating, let's take a look at dietary strategies that might help you lose control less often. Could your eating habits be partly responsible for the problem? This chapter will provide you with keys for understanding and tips for reexamining how you eat . . . and give you back some freedom in the bargain.

Let's forget the word *diet*

Are you tired of constantly watching what you eat, trying to lose weight, and making many failed attempts without any real long-term success? What if, for once, you forgot about restricting your food and took pleasure in eating again?

We saw the following clearly in the preceding chapter: although restricted diets succeed in the short term, their long-term results are much less impressive. Once off the diet, people either go back to their old habits and start binge eating again or experience a slowdown in their metabolism, which inevitably means they put the weight back on. Constantly imposing restrictions on yourself to lose or maintain weight means that your body no longer relies on sensations of hunger and fullness and exists in a hyper-controlled state.

If you have episodes of binge eating, you must stay connected to what you really want. Feel like some chocolate but your inner voice tells you to have a low-fat yogurt? Maybe so, but you're still likely to dive into a box of chocolate cookies later in the day. It would have been wiser to have a few squares of chocolate and fully enjoy them, thus responding more satisfactorily to your true desire. By doing so, you replace the fear of not having the right to certain foods, of missing out on them, with the satisfaction of having the right to eat everything—a diet revolution that reflects one of food's universal roles: to give us pleasure!

Of course, this behaviour is hard to adopt if you binge eat every day and if certain specific foods trigger bingeing. The best thing to do is to reintroduce these kinds of foods gradually (we'll return to this in the next chapter).

Guidelines for "not dieting"

- You acknowledge that there are no "forbidden" foods: You can eat anything: some foods are part of your daily diet; others you eat only occasionally.

- You're aware of your hunger and stop eating when you're full.

- You don't eat for comfort when faced with a difficult situation.

- You weigh yourself no more than once a month.

- When you eat, you enjoy every mouthful, taking the time to really taste your food.

You don't have to eat perfectly

Eating is one of life's great pleasures. Of course some foods are more nutritious than others, but categorizing them as good or bad affects our relationship with them. Instead, let's just say there are foods we like to put on the menu regularly and others we eat only occasionally.

True or false?

It's important to count calories to know the exact amount of food to eat every day.

False

This approach works well for some people, but it's not recommended for everybody. It's healthier to recognize your body's fullness signals than to calculate everything.

If most of the time you eat foods included in *Canada's Food Guide* and fruit- or yogurt-based desserts are lifestyle staples for you, then it's normal and completely acceptable to spoil yourself with sweets or other gourmet treats from time to time. In other words, if you eat yogurt for dessert every night of the week, you have every right to enjoy chocolate cake at a restaurant on Saturday night. Similarly, if you eat whole grain toast for breakfast almost every morning, it's totally acceptable to eat a croissant with the family on Sundays.

Eating well means putting healthy foods you like on the menu as often as possible, but it also means enjoying small, less nutritious treats from time to time. Eating everything without guilt may seem utopian for many people who struggle with binge eating or bulimia. You have to give yourself the time needed to rediscover this healthy relationship with food. Your dietitian and your psychologist will help you get there.

What exactly does *eating well* mean?

When you've spent years struggling with out-of-control eating, you get to the point where you no longer know what a balanced diet is.

Should you count calories or weigh foods?

Neither, actually, since strictly controlling your dietary intake will only trigger more bingeing episodes. The best idea is to aim for the *balanced plate*! The plate provides a concrete model for healthy eating. If vegetables fill half the plate, proteins one quarter, and grain products the other quarter, then the plate contains all essential nutrients. Sticking to the balanced plate at noon and in the evening does away with the need to count calories.

Variety is also key. Some foods are reassuring for people who have a difficult relationship with food. You have to step out of your comfort zone to try new foods or reintroduce those you thought were forbidden. But reintroduce such foods one at a time—say, socially first (with family, among friends). For example, if a chocolate dessert causes anxiety, eat it at a party in the company of friends. The fact that everyone has a piece and enjoys it makes it a pleasant, less stressful experience.

For dessert, your best options are milk products, soy-based items, and fruit. If you crave a decadent dessert, make a point of eating it slowly and really savouring it (see the mindfulness exercise on page 80), and stop eating when you reach the point of fullness. Eating this way is especially difficult when you're just beginning to take control. Start with safer food items first, and then introduce anxiety-inducing foods when you're with someone close in whom you have confidence, or with your therapist.

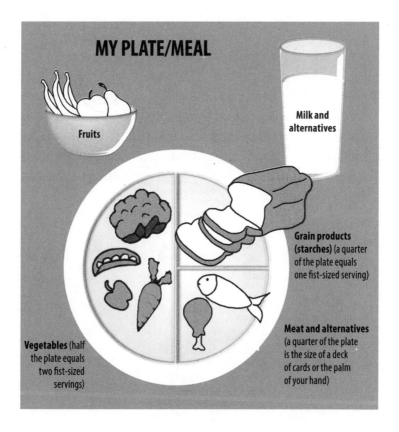

MY PLATE/MEAL

Fruits

Milk and alternatives

Grain products (starches) (a quarter of the plate equals one fist-sized serving)

Meat and alternatives (a quarter of the plate is the size of a deck of cards or the palm of your hand)

Vegetables (half the plate equals two fist-sized servings)

Better controlling your appetite to reduce binge eating

Many people who watch their diet are perfectly in control (sometimes too much so!) during the day: whole grain bread in the morning, tuna salad at noon, and fruit for snacks. Yet in the evening they lose control and eat whatever is handy, thereby taking in a lot of extra calories. Unsurprisingly, their weight constantly fluctuates. Here are the key principles for overcoming loss of control:

The 3–3–3 rule

To stabilize your body's natural weight and thus prevent any future weight gain triggered by repetitive dieting, you have to work with your body. Reassure it that there will be no more periods of starvation and that it can stop being constantly on the alert. By following the 3–3–3 rule, you can give yourself this internal reassurance.

3 meals → **3** snacks → every **3** hours

An example of a day following the 3-3-3 rule

6:30 a.m. Breakfast
- 2 pieces of whole grain toast
- almond butter
- 2 clementines
- a glass of milk

9:30 a.m. Morning snack
- a fruit yogurt sprinkled with chia seeds, and a nectarine

12:30 p.m. Lunch
- 1 whole wheat pita with a small tin of tuna
- carrots, cucumbers, and peppers with hummus
- rice pudding

3:30 p.m. Afternoon snack
- 2 rye crackers and 1½ oz. of cheese

6:30 p.m. Dinner
- 3 oz. of grilled chicken (the size of the palm of your hand)
- quinoa with vegetables (the size of a fist)
- arugula and tomato salad
- 1 yogurt

9:30 p.m. Evening snack
- a package of instant oatmeal cooked in soy milk

Breakfast is the most important meal of the day.

True

After fasting overnight for 8 to 12 hours, it's important to refuel to better face the new day. Ideally, breakfast should include fruit, a cereal product, and a source of protein, such as milk, soy milk, eggs, cheese, nuts, seeds, or yogurt. Not hungry in the morning? Maybe it's because you snack in the evening. If you're not hungry in the morning, have a nutritious snack around 9:30 a.m.—say, whole wheat crackers, cheese, and fruit, or yogurt and a homemade muffin. Don't go without protein in the morning.

The evening meal should be the lightest.

True

Since we're more physically active during the day than in the evening, of course we need more energy then to carry out our tasks. But since noon-hour breaks are often limited to 30 minutes, understandably the evening meal is often the main meal of the day. By listening to your fullness signals, you'll be able to avoid eating too much at night, your digestion will be better, and you'll sleep better.

To get into the habit of eating this way, start by trying to follow the schedule without paying too much attention to the content of the plate. From our observations, this takes two weeks, with the help of the food diary in chapter 5 (see page 104). Eat normal, everyday foods—a chicken sandwich, or a bowl of cereal with a banana, for example. Or vary what you eat by aiming for the balanced plate described on page 29. The goal is to get into the habit of eating by the clock, every three hours or so.

It's normal *not* to feel hungry on this schedule at the beginning. Ask yourself how long it's been since you last ate three meals and three snacks, day after day, for weeks or months. Your natural hunger and feelings of fullness will come back, but you'll have to be patient and kind to your body. This new way of eating can also be a good opportunity to learn to cook, to "travel" via exotic dishes. Should it be India or Thailand this evening? This epicurean approach helps us to reconnect with the taste of different foods, to eat more slowly and let go of our food taboos.

Serotonin: the key to control for "emotional" eaters

In her book *The Serotonin Solution*,[1] Dr. Judith J. Wurtman, a researcher at the Massachusetts Institute of Technology, suggests a way of eating that makes you feel fuller and reduces the frequency of binge eating episodes related to emotions. The key, she found in her research, is the neurotransmitter *serotonin*, which regulates a number of body functions, including dietary and sexual behaviour. Serotonin has the ability to enhance mood, so much so that many anti-depressants seek to increase its availability. Some foods can increase the amount of serotonin circulating in our bodies. In fact, the more serotonin we have, the more we're in control of what we eat.

When we're in the grip of "psychological" hunger (triggered by an emotion), the body craves carbohydrates in various forms (donuts, crackers, chips, bread, cereal). This is normal, since high-carbohydrate foods are the only ones, when eaten in sufficient amounts, that increase the serotonin in circulation. Low-carbohydrate diets (including a keto diet), which are still very popular, are not at all recommended for "emotional" eaters. Such diets deplete the carbohydrate reserves in the liver and muscles and cause fluid loss, as well. Feeling thinner, many people like the result, but as soon as they reintroduce carbohydrates, reserves build up again and their weight inevitably goes up. What's more, they may even have sugar cravings!

Managing binge eating calls for having carbohydrates at every meal, including snacks. If you want to avoid losing control in the evening, you must eat enough grain products (or starches) during the day. They will preferably be whole grain so as to make you feel even fuller. (Fruits don't have the same effect.) These foods should be low in fat, as this nutrient slows down digestion and serotonin production. Too many people watch their calories so closely during the day that they eat only yogurt and fruit in the morning and salad at lunch—there's nothing worse for triggering binge eating in the evening!

PMS: dying for sugar!

The hormonal changes that occur before a menstrual period affect serotonin levels, which makes the neurotransmitter less effective in managing appetite control at that time. To avoid binge eating, increase the amount of grain products for three to five days before your period. Take care, as well, to eat grain products (or starches) at every one of your three meals, as well as to include two mainly carbohydrate snacks (crackers, oatmeal, cereal bars, etc.).

Examples of grain products to include in meals and snacks:

- whole grain bread (1 or 2 slices)
- whole wheat bagel or English muffin (1)
- whole wheat pita (1)
- pasta, rice, couscous, quinoa (½–1 cup)
- crackers (2–5)
- low-sugar cereals* (½–1 cup)
- oatmeal (¾–1 cup)
- low-sugar cereal bar* (1)

Still craving sugar? Choose dried dates, a little dark chocolate, or a chocolate soy pudding.

---

* Try to choose breakfast cereals with fewer than 5 grams of sugar per 1 oz. serving and cereal bars containing fewer than 8 grams of sugar each.

A personal thoughts diary: to gain a better understanding

A personal thoughts diary is a useful tool for better understanding our eating habits, especially for making us aware of our emotional and psychological relationship with food. It's a way to get to know our food behaviours non-judgmentally: Where and when do we consume food? What exactly do we eat? What thoughts or emotions do we experience at those times? Do we feel like we're losing control?

Here's an example that may inspire you to keep your own diary:

DAY & TIME	FOOD EATEN	CONTEXT (Where? With whom?)	FEELING OF LOSING CONTROL?	THOUGHT	EMOTION
Tuesday 5:30 p.m.	Large bag of chips	Alone in my car after work	Yes	I'm exhausted; I don't want to be alone at home.	Fatigue Loneliness
Saturday 3:00 p.m.	10 chocolate cookies 3 slices of pizza	Alone at home	Yes	I shouldn't just do nothing. I'm lazy!	Anger Shame Sadness
Sunday 6:00 p.m.	3 beers Double serving of fries	With my parents and my sister at my parents' place	Yes	My mother made me fries; she knows it's hard for me and she made them anyway.	Anger Powerlessness

DAY & TIME	FOOD EATEN	CONTEXT (Where? With whom?)	FEELING OF LOSING CONTROL?	THOUGHT	EMOTION
Thursday 7:00 p.m.	Spare ribs with fries and dessert	At a restaurant with colleagues	No	Everybody is having ribs, so me too!	Fatigue Festive
Saturday 9:00 p.m.	Ice cream (2 big bowls) and half a bag of chips	Alone in bed at home	Yes	I had a blind date tonight. I didn't go—I was too afraid I'd be rejected.	Shame Sadness Loneliness
Friday 6:00 p.m.	Tuna salad	At a restaurant with friends for a birthday	No	I'm the only one not having birthday cake. Nobody wants to see a fat woman eating cake!	Shame Injustice Pride
Tuesday 5:00 p.m.	Large piece of cheese 30 crackers I glass of wine	At home with the kids	Yes	I have to make dinner for the kids; I'm exhausted— they make so much noise.	Irritation Fatigue

We suggest you make a note of everything you eat for several weeks, without recording calories or measuring the food.

When an eating disorder has existed for a long time, sometimes our emotions are harder to understand—as if, over time and as we ignore basic signals like hunger, the wires have little by little become disconnected. A list is often a big help in identifying emotions. You'll find one in appendix 2 of this book. Start with the discomfort you feel or the thought you've identified, and then ask yourself more detailed questions as you peruse the list.

As you read, see if you can pick out themes for yourself based on your diary. In other words, can you discern thoughts, emotions, situations, or contexts that recur and contribute to triggering binge eating?

To do this, ask yourself the following questions:

- Does the binge eating attack always occur in a particular situation?

- What emotion or thought is most often present when I lose control around food?

- Does this happen on days when I haven't eaten enough at mealtimes or snack times?

These elements will help you pinpoint what you need to work on to break the binge eating cycle.

"For me, the most important words are *health* and *balance*. In 2009 I was diagnosed with lumbar stenosis; I could no longer stand up without terrible pain, I was overweight, and I lacked energy. Why, you ask? Because like many women, I was too busy looking after my family, after those I love, to look after myself, and I got sick. I had to review my priorities to be able to take my life in hand again and regain my health.

I started by changing my diet, to lose my extra weight but also to reduce the inflammation in my body.

As I lost weight, I began to write down how I felt, because I had a basic need to note everything I ate, felt, and did. My diary became my best ally. Through my writing, I realized why I was eating my emotions and why I had paid so little attention to myself. I even understood the factors that made me binge eat! Now that I'm aware of all those harmful things, I'm able to understand what my healthy choices mean to me and put them into practice. I know that I'll struggle with this all my life, because bad habits often come rushing back. But by continuing to write in my health diary, I'm taking care of myself and staying aware of the positive attitudes I have to adopt to stay healthy and feel good about myself."

—Natacha Watier

What should you eat to feel more satisfied?

Once we stop counting calories, we need to focus on foods that fill us up quickly. We also have to trust our feelings of fullness to stop eating when we've satisfied our hunger (we'll come back to this in chapter 5).

High-protein foods (meat, poultry, fish, eggs, nuts, cheese, legumes) and those high in fibre (legumes, whole grain cereals, chia seeds, etc.) are particularly filling.

True or false?

Everyone should avoid gluten.

False

Despite its popularity, a gluten-free diet is not for everyone—just people with celiac disease (1 percent of the population), as well as those who are hypersensitive to gluten (3 to 5 percent of the population). For everyone else, the advantages of whole wheat, whole rye, and other grains are widely recognized by science. Gluten-free foods are often lower in fibre and higher in sugar than ordinary grain products are. They're seldom the best choice. Avoiding gluten in your diet is not advisable unless your healthcare professional recommends you do so.

The more rapidly absorbed sugar a food contains, the more it will destabilize blood sugar, which risks causing a new craving. By avoiding rapidly absorbed sugars (honey, jam, white sugar, candies, etc.) and instead choosing foods with a low *glycemic index*, you avoid blood sugar fluctuations and promote a feeling of fullness. The glycemic index is influenced by the presence of other foods (for example, fat lowers it) and by cooking (pasta al dente has a lower index than well-cooked pasta does). (See the glycemic index table on page 53.)

A few tips for feeling full faster

✓ Increase fibre consumption.

High-fibre foods provide a feeling of fullness. Whole wheat pasta is more filling than pasta made from refined flour. The same is true of whole grain bread and high-fibre cereal. Take the time to read nutrition information labels and choose products with the highest amount of fibre.

✓ Eat enough protein.

Like fibre, protein satisfies hunger. So be sure to include a protein source in every meal (egg, cheese, or peanut butter in the morning; meat, poultry, fish, or legumes at noon and in the evening). Protein-rich foods are frequently overlooked in the morning and at noon. This is a shame, because hard-to-control cravings are then likely to occur during the day.

✓ **Limit sugary drinks.**

It's a proven fact that the calories we drink are far less sustaining than those we eat. Keep a close eye on all drinks (fruit cocktails, soft drinks, energy drinks, juice, iced tea, flavoured coffees, and so on). Water, milk, and plant-based drinks remain the best beverage choices. Tea and coffee, with no added sugar, are also good options.

✓ **Eat lots of vegetables.**

Noon and night, be sure to fill half your plate with vegetables (see the balanced plate on page 29). The more vegetables you eat, the less hungry you'll be! To reduce hunger, you can also start a meal with a soup, a glass of vegetable juice, or a salad. These are also the best starters to choose in a restaurant.

✓ **Plan nutritious snacks.**

Snacks are a big help in curbing cravings during the day. Ideally, they combine carbohydrates and protein, so as to stabilize blood sugar effectively and limit cravings. Here are a few ideas for snacks to include in the morning or afternoon to boost your energy, as well as help you hold on until your next meal:

10 snack ideas that provide a good carbohydrate-protein ratio

1. A small flavoured Greek yogurt

2. A small bunch of grapes with cottage cheese

3. A handful of dried cranberries with a handful of almonds*

4. Low-sodium vegetable juice and a hard-boiled egg

5. A slice of whole grain bread with peanut butter

6. An apple and one individual packet of cheese

7. A few crackers with hummus

8. A soy beverage in a tetra pack and a handful of pumpkin seeds

9. An apple and a handful of roasted chickpeas

10. Raw vegetables and a handful of peanuts

The afternoon snack is without doubt the most important one in terms of binge eating. It helps you better resist the temptation to dive into the fridge or cupboards when you get home.

---

* Since we avoid weighing or measuring foods, we usually talk about nuts in terms of a handful. A handful (fist closed) is a good serving. Individual packets of nuts (20 to 30 grams) are also good options. No need to calculate!

For people who eat late, it's a good idea to have two afternoon snacks, one at around 3:00 p.m. and the other around 5:30 p.m., to avoid raiding the cupboards the minute you get in. Having a snack at the office just before leaving is a good solution for people who tend to lose control when they get home. Eating a little something also lowers the risk of stopping at the convenience store on the way. So, for example, when you take your vegetables and piece of cheese to work, you limit how much you eat and, even more important, you won't find yourself at the mercy of the entire block of cheese sitting on the kitchen counter!

True or false?

Food eaten outside mealtimes makes you fat.

False

On the contrary, when you eat satisfying snacks, you'll eat less at the next meal. A snack combining carbohydrates and protein (see our snack ideas on page 43) will be sustaining enough to keep you from diving into the fridge when you get home.

The evening snack is important, especially for people who get up at night to eat. Since we're often prone to binge eat in the evening, it's better to opt for a less risky snack. You'll be less likely to get carried away by a bowl of yogurt with fruit than by a bowl of cereal, which may lead to a second bowl . . . Sometimes just a soy drink or a glass of milk will do in the evening.

Night eaters?

People who eat during the night may have hypoglycemia without knowing it. Since blood sugar falls sharply in the middle of the night, these people wake up and invariably go looking for sources of carbohydrates. To avoid waking up at night, which interferes with sleep and weight control, plan for a snack just before going to bed. Because it's a source of carbohydrates and soluble fibre, oatmeal cooked in milk is an excellent choice that helps stabilize blood sugar levels. You can also choose a Greek yogurt and add some chia seeds.

When you mend your relationship with food by eating to satisfy actual hunger in a healthy way, without calorie counting and by exercising for enjoyment, your weight will remain stable. What a relief to no longer experience the yo-yo effect!

What about your intestines?

Research in recent years has emphasized the importance of balanced intestinal flora for many health problems. In fact, we now know that a large portion of serotonin is secreted by the cells in our intestines and that our microbial flora (or *microbiota*) may be directly related to our emotions—quite a piece of news! Approaches for intervention are not yet clear, but we can bet that the coming years will reveal the importance of probiotics for modifying our mood and even our eating habits.

The diversity of microbial flora is associated positively with health. Overweight people have been found to have less diversified flora. Diet explains most microbiota variations.

10 tips for balancing your microbiota

Increase your consumption of:

1. Fibre (new research suggests that intakes of 50 to 55 grams per day would be desirable, or roughly twice the current recommendations)

2. Fruits and vegetables (7 to 10 servings a day)

3. Fish (for its anti-inflammatory properties)

4. Good sources of polyphenols (raisins, wine, cocoa, berries)

5. Fermented products (kefir, kombucha, sauerkraut, kimchi, yogurt)

6. Prebiotics (like inulin) that feed the intestine's micro-organisms

Limit your consumption of:

7. Sugar (this can affect the permeability of the intestinal membrane and thus destabilize the organism)

8. Saturated fats (including coconut oil)

9. Products containing emulsifiers (ice cream, commercially produced salad dressings)

10. Sweeteners

Remember

✓ Say goodbye to diets: they can trigger binge eating.
✓ Respect the 3–3–3 rule: eat 3 meals and 3 snacks, every 3 hours.
✓ Adopt the balanced plate.
✓ Keep a thoughts diary to better understand the situations in which you give in to cravings.
✓ Select foods that promote fullness (protein, fibre, foods with a low glycemic index).
✓ Choose foods that promote a balanced microbiota.

CHAPTER

COMING TO TERMS
WITH TRIGGER FOODS

We now know that what creates a trigger food is primarily the fact that we don't allow ourselves to eat it. However, everyone will tell you that there are some foods they can't put into their mouths without invariably losing control. Depending on the person, these may include chocolate, cookies, croissants, crackers, jam, honey, chips, sometimes even bread or pasta. These foods have a common characteristic: they're rich in carbohydrates and have a high glycemic index (GI).

The relationship between the glycemic index* and dietary control is complex. Consuming foods with a high glycemic index seems to encourage hunger to return more quickly and increase subsequent energy intake, compared with the consumption of low-GI foods. As far as we know, however, there have been no specific studies evaluating glycemic index and hunger in people with an eating behaviour disorder. The ability of high-GI foods to trigger binge eating remains to be demonstrated, but this is a very interesting line of research. We know that sugar makes us feel full. But there might be more to the story: might it not be possible that consuming high-GI foods causes a blood sugar disruption that influences appetite or even dietary control? The hypersecretion of insulin following the ingestion of high-GI foods causes a significant drop in blood sugar (without, however, reaching actual hypoglycemia) that might lead to a renewed desire to eat. This remains an avenue worth exploring.

---

* The glycemic index reflects the speed with which a food's carbohydrates are digested, converted, and reach the bloodstream in the form of glucose. It reflects the increase in blood glucose after the ingestion of 50 g of carbohydrates from a food, by comparing it with the increase in blood glucose after the ingestion of 50 g of carbohydrates from a reference food (glucose or white bread).

One thing for sure is that at the start of a process aiming to break the binge eating cycle, it's wise to eliminate all "trigger" foods (the list of these foods will be unique to each person). Some people will never want to reintroduce these foods, feeling they are like a drug. Some compulsive eaters describe eating their trigger foods as "going on a bender." In fact, members of Overeaters Anonymous talk about abstaining from sugar and avoid all forms of concentrated sugar.

Does sugar, like drugs, create dependency?

Animal studies have often shown that sugar can create a dependency similar to drugs by significantly increasing *dopamine*, a neurotransmitter linked to pleasure and the reward system.[1] Studies in humans, however, have not succeeded in clearly demonstrating that sugar creates a dependency similar to drugs.[2] While some brain regions associated with pleasure are quite active when foods high in sugar (and often also high in fats) are eaten, it appears that chronic stress and low morale (or depression) are stronger predictors of loss of control.

Our opinion? If you binge several times a week, we advise you to remove from your environment those foods that trigger compulsive eating. However, we encourage you to reintroduce them, over several months, first in safe environments (at friends' homes or in restaurants, for example) and then gradually at home.

Glycemic index (GI) of foods grouped in various categories*

FOOD CATEGORIES	LOW GI (< 55)	MEDIUM GI (55 to 70)	HIGH GI (> 70)
GRAIN PRODUCTS			
Cereals	All-Bran, All-Bran Buds (which have psyllium), steel cut oats, oat bran	shredded wheat, quick-cooking oats	Rice Krispies, cornflakes, bran flakes, Cheerios, instant oats
Breads	Multigrain bread/12-grain bread, stoneground whole wheat bread, pumpernickel	Whole wheat, rye, sourdough, pita breads	White bread, white bagels, kaiser rolls
Rice/other grains/pasta	Pasta cooked al dente, noodles, par-boiled or precooked rice, barley, bulgur	Basmati rice, brown rice, couscous	Instant rice
FRUITS AND VEGETABLES			
Vegetables	Sweet potatoes, peas, yams	Raw carrots, baked potatoes with skin, new potatoes, corn	Baked potatoes without skin, mashed potatoes, parsnips, rutabaga, winter squash

* Sources: Canadian Sugar Institute and Canadian Diabetes Association

(continued on next page)

FOOD CATEGORIES	LOW GI (< 55)	MEDIUM GI (55 to 70)	HIGH GI (> 70)
FRUITS AND VEGETABLES			
Fruits	Apples, oranges, strawberries, peaches, cherries, grapes	Bananas, raisins, apricots	Watermelon, dried dates
Juices	Apple juice, orange juice, grapefruit juice, tomato juice	Grape juice, cranberry cocktail	
DAIRY PRODUCTS			
	Milk, plain yogurt, sweetened yogurt, chocolate milk	Sweetened condensed milk	
LEGUMES			
	Lentils, red beans, soy beans, chick-peas, baked beans, split peas		
SWEETENERS			
	Fructose	Table sugar (sucrose), brown sugar, honey	Glucose (GI = 100)
OTHER			
		Pea soup, popcorn	Rice cakes, french fries, crackers

Regaining control over trigger foods step by step

Here's how to reincorporate foods you consider problematic into your diet:

1. **Make a list of your trigger foods and remove them temporarily from your home.**
   The first thing to do is to draw up your list of trigger foods—it will vary from person to person. Remove these foods temporarily from your home. Without chips, ice cream, and chocolate spread in the house, you lessen the risk of a binge eating episode. If you can't resist an eating binge, you'll have to take the car or walk to the corner

store, giving you extra time to think carefully about your decision.

If you have teenagers or children you don't want to deprive, buy flavours you like less to reduce initial temptations. Do BBQ chips tempt you less than vinegar chips? Those are the ones to choose.

2. **Eat some of your trigger foods in a safe environment (with friends or at a restaurant).**

   When everything is under control at home, that's when to begin the gradual reintroduction of problematic foods.

   You've compiled a list of the foods that make you afraid of gaining weight or that can trigger a binge if you eat them. Now divide them according to how intense your fear is. Here's an example of one client's trigger food reintroduction list:

FEAR INTENSITY	TRIGGER FOODS
Low	Peanut butter, breakfast cereals
Medium	Crackers, store-bought muffins, pasta
High	Chips, store-bought cookies, croissants, ice cream, chocolate

First reintroduce low-intensity foods in a safe context. For example, this client began eating peanut butter again by having two small containers in a restaurant at breakfast on a slice of bread. She savoured her toast without fear of it turning into an eating binge. She thus created a new association: "I can eat this food without it having a negative result."

You're at a birthday party and everyone is having a piece of cake? Have one, too! Serve yourself a piece like everybody else and enjoy it. Since the cake isn't in your house, you don't run the risk of diving into the leftovers as soon as the guests have left.

And remember: avoid "all or nothing" thinking. It's not black or white; the day isn't ruined just because you ate a piece of cake. One piece of cake does not in any way spoil the day. Repeat this sentence to yourself a few times and do this for every food that causes anxiety.

3. Reintroduce trigger foods at home one by one.
Beginning with the least problematic foods (for instance, dark chocolate instead of milk chocolate), reintroduce treats into your house and then eat them when you really want to and not to soothe an emotion. At the beginning, we recommend eating them in the presence of someone close to you in whom you have confidence, and not when you're alone.

Let's look again at the example of the client who reintroduced peanut butter at a restaurant. Since the experience was positive, she bought a jar of peanut butter to have at home and began to eat some on bread every morning, reminding herself she could eat it every morning if she wanted and could buy another jar when she finished that one. As a result, her "I'm going to eat it all so there won't be any more in the house" kind of thinking diminished as the weeks went by. Each food can be reintroduced gradually in this way, mindfully and by creating a positive association, as opposed to the negative emotions that follow a loss of control.

A few tips to enhance your chances of success when you reintroduce trigger foods

1. Eat sitting at the table.

2. Serve your food on a plate.

3. Once you have served your portion of food, put the containers in the cupboards or the fridge.

4. Avoid TV and other distractions while you eat.

5. Eat each mouthful more slowly.

6. Pay attention to the texture, aroma, colour, and flavour of the food—the way you taste a good wine.

7. Pay attention to your feeling of hunger and the point at which you're full.

"As far back as I can remember, I've always had trouble managing my behaviour toward food. Yet I was raised in a loving and well-off family, where everything was available.

My relationship with refined sugar is still a source of anxiety for me. I feel dependent on it. I've been sober and completely off alcohol and drugs for over 24 years. My binge eating and dependency on refined sugar have led me to sink to the lowest depths of my life.

When I quit drinking, I filled my internal emptiness with sugar—for a year and a half, during my eating binges, I'd stuff myself with at least two dozen donuts, entire boxes of chocolate, cake icing in secret . . .

I went from having a slender body to being a huge mass of fat: I put on more than 250 pounds and I weighed over 400 pounds for almost five years.

My compulsive eating led me into destructive, manipulative behaviours where I almost went crazy. I've lost count of the number of times I invented last-minute errands so I could leave my family and go get myself some SUGAR.

Here's what these binges made me do:

- Eat alone in my car.
- Change stores so as to not be recognized and look like "a fat pig."
- Throw my garbage into the street, so as not to be found out.

- *Hide chocolate and get up at night to eat it.*
- *Eat barely thawed food.*

In short, an obsession—yes, literally an obsession—with eating sugar, no matter what the cost, while getting fatter and fatter, and not doing anything to stop it . . .

I was lucky enough to undergo bariatric surgery 14 years ago. The doctor warned me that binge eating disorder was stronger than any operation and that, like 8 people out of 10, I might regain the weight in the long term. I challenged myself to be among those who would never regain the weight lost, and up to now I've succeeded.

Not only did I lose my excess weight but I've been able to rediscover a body I accept. Binge eating will always be MY GREATEST STRUGGLE. Sometimes I relapse, but I now know this happens when I haven't done what I'm supposed to:

- *My meals aren't planned, I don't have my snacks with me, and my fridge is empty.*
- *I've had one mouthful of something sweet and I tell myself, 'Oh well, I might as well go whole hog.'*
- *I've eaten a trigger food.*
- *I'm right in the middle of PMS.*

I will always have to be disciplined about food. My binge eating is a serious emotional disease. Nowadays I have to meditate on what I want to be, I share my experiences with other women, and I have a profession that requires me to stay in excellent shape.

Yes, recovery is possible. Perfection? No. But who doesn't eat too much from time to time? What you have to do is recognize the point at which binge eating takes over . . . it's a hell of a disease.

My binge eating will always be my greatest weakness, but when you do what you have to and are disciplined about it, it can become a great source of self-knowledge.

I encourage you to face up to it, recognize it, and try to take control of it."

—Julie Déry, personal trainer, life coach, and lecturer

Weight loss and binge eating

Many binge eaters come to see us with the goal of losing weight. Weight loss is not the main goal of sessions with a therapist. On the other hand, weight loss can be part of the process. Ask yourself these questions before embarking on this path:

- Have I managed to stabilize my diet, my weight, and my binges?

- Do I need to lose weight because of worrisome medical results (cholesterol, heart problems, reflux, high blood pressure, sleep apnea)?

- Am I able to follow nutritional recommendations while being flexible and gentle with myself and not by adopting them like rules in a new diet?

If you've answered yes to these three questions, a gradual weight-loss approach is possible.

Your food plan

A restrictive diet, as we've noted, triggers compulsive eating, and it's therefore more appropriate to follow a food plan that aims to restructure food intake. Having lost all baseline references to what a balanced diet adapted to need is, binge eaters no longer know what to eat or how much. Our initial assessment enables us to establish individual needs and estimate basal metabolic rate. The resulting plan will be as flexible as possible, ranging from 1,500 to 1,900 calories for a woman and 1,800 to 2,100 calories for a man. However, we don't usually tell you what your calorie range is, to avoid making it an obsession.

Patients are frequently surprised at the amount and variety of food they can eat every day and firmly believe they will never lose weight eating so much. Yet when binge eating episodes that often result in an energy intake of more than 3,000 calories are controlled, long-term weight loss is considerable. Of course, the ultimate objective of a food plan is not so much weight loss but the control of binge eating. Too restrictive a plan leaves people hungry and susceptible to future binge eating attacks. A food plan consisting of three meals and three snacks is often best. As in the diet for people with hypoglycemia, the snacks usually combine carbohydrates and protein (a piece of fruit and a piece of cheese, for example), which seems to better control cravings. Again, the food plan encourages a return to a normal diet rather than it being a weight-loss diet.

Incorporating physical exercise

If formal physical exercise isn't something you enjoy, consider incorporating physical exercise into your daily activities. You can do this by getting yourself a step counter (pedometer) or using an app on your smartphone. To lose weight gradually, try to walk more than 7,000 steps a day.

Making small changes to your daily routine will help you achieve your goal:

- Walk while talking on the phone.

- Use public transport.

- Park your car at the far end of the parking lot.

- Suggest to your colleagues that they get out and walk with you during your lunch break.

- Don't use the elevator or escalator—take the stairs instead.

- Do the chores yourself (shovel snow in the winter, cut the grass in the summer, etc.).[3]

We'll revisit the benefits of physical activity in chapter 6.

Eating fat makes you fat.

False

If this were true, everyone in Mediterranean countries would be overweight. What we now know is that we can eat more fats than we thought, as long as they're good fats. Nuts, seeds, avocados, and olive oil are definitely part of a balanced diet. It's not one nutrient in particular (e.g., fat or sugar) that triggers weight gain but, instead, eating more calories than we burn off.

Some foods melt fat.

False

To date no food is known to stimulate fat loss. Only a calorie intake lower than what we burn can melt fat reserves.

Food combinations encourage weight loss.

False

We all have the enzymes required to digest mixed meals. There is no need to separate fruit and protein from starches. Eat the mixtures you enjoy and don't worry about it!

Remember

✓ In some people, specific foods (often high in fat and sugar) trigger compulsive eating. The list of foods varies from one person to another, as does the degree of anxiety they cause.

✓ Avoiding binge trigger foods may be useful in the short term, but it's not a desirable long-term solution. We suggest gradually reintroducing trigger foods in a safe context to create a positive association with them, so you no longer feel threatened when they're around.

✓ If food compulsions have been stabilized, and if you are overweight and your extra pounds are affecting your health, a gradual weight-loss approach is suggested. The diet will be slightly calorie reduced and take into account the nutrition guidelines discussed in chapter 2.

LEARNING TO MANAGE YOUR EMOTIONS AND MODIFY YOUR THINKING

Many people who binge eat say they feel emotions more strongly than the average person does. Food acts as a source of comfort when dealing with certain painful or very strong emotions. But eating too much also has serious consequences.

Breaking free of the comfort food trap

Your boss criticizes your work, and feeling hurt, you head for the vending machine to buy a chocolate bar. Your romantic partner is away for the week, and out of boredom, you snack every evening. You're about to have an important interview, and the night before, feeling stressed out, you dive into a tub of ice cream.

Many people find comfort in food and use it to deal with various emotions they have trouble handling any other way. But this behaviour brings only temporary relief. You have to develop a range of responses to any given situation. Here are a few examples:

I'm bored:

- I call a friend.

- I go out for a walk while listening to my favourite music.

- I call a support group.

I'm angry with someone:

- I write a letter.

- I assert myself with whomever has caused this emotion.

- I call a friend to talk about it.

I'm feeling anxious:

- I do a meditation or breathing exercise.*

- I have a bath while playing relaxing music.

Other possibilities to add to your range of reactions:

- Drink a large glass of water.

- Have a nap.

- Do something for someone else (for example, look after a friend's child while they do their shopping, send a comforting message to someone going through a tough time, or simply help someone out).

- Practise yoga.

---

* For training yourself to breathe in and out at a regular rhythm, several free mobile apps on cardiac coherence may be of interest, like CardioZen and Respiroguide. Good breathing facilitates the release of dopamine and serotonin—two neurotransmitters key to managing eating behaviours—within a few minutes.

In addition, if you have a tendency to let yourself be overwhelmed by negative emotions, try not to overreact to situations. Be creative and turn them into something constructive. Your boss criticized you? So much the better—it will help you improve your work performance or give you the opportunity to assert yourself. Lonely without your partner? Make the most of it by doing something you want to do and never have time to: meet up with old friends, go to the theatre or the movies; use the week to do what you enjoy—100 percent of the time, without any compromises. Stressed out by an interview? Prepare yourself well, do yoga exercises, or get out and play a sport. These activities will give you more satisfaction!

True or false?

We can learn to control our emotions.

False

It's impossible to "control" our emotions. Emotions are a psychological reflex to our interpretation of a given situation. It's important to understand that emotions have a function, a role. They are our alarm system. Their purpose is to signal a need and help us to respond to it. We can't control our emotions, but we can manage them better and change the way we interpret a given situation.

Modifying thoughts that distort reality

In cognitive behavioural therapy, the most effective psychological approach currently known for treating binge eating, the aim is to change behaviours and emotions by modifying the automatic thoughts or beliefs that distort our perception of reality. Of course, we first have to understand what a cognitive distortion is.

Cognitive distortions[1]

The term *cognitive distortion* comes to us from psychiatrist Aaron T. Beck. It denotes a way of handling information that results in an error in thinking and thus causes a series of reflections and negative emotions. Different kinds of cognitive distortions include:

- **All or nothing: a tendency to think in terms of white or black, good or bad.**
  Example: I ate a chip; I wasn't supposed to eat any; while I'm at it, I'll finish the bag, since the day is ruined anyway.

- **Overgeneralization: a single unfortunate event viewed as part of an endless series of failures.**
  Example: I didn't manage to get any exercise today; it's always going to be the same story.

- **Filtering: dwelling so much on a negative detail that your entire view of reality is distorted.**
  Example: I've managed to eat in a healthy way all week, but I've been dwelling so much on last night's binge that I have the impression my week is a failure.

- **Rejecting the positive: rejecting neutral or positive events to preserve a negative image of things, even when this does not correspond to reality.**
  Example: People tell me I'm beautiful and look healthy just to please me. They don't really think that.

- **Jumping to conclusions:**
  - **Undue interpretation: arbitrarily deciding that someone feels negatively toward you, without checking to see if it's true.**
    Example: I met my partner's sister for the first time this weekend. She said almost nothing to me; I'm certain she doesn't like me.

  - **Mistaken prediction: predicting the worst and being convinced that this prediction is confirmed by the facts.**
    Example: My longing to be part of a couple is doomed to failure. Every time I meet a man, he ends the relationship after a few months.

- **Exaggeration and minimization: magnifying the importance of some things (your mistakes or others' successes) and minimizing the importance of other things (your qualities or your neighbour's imperfections).**
  Example: My colleague gets regular exercise just for fun, but I could never do that.

- **Emotional reasoning: assuming your negative feelings necessarily reflect reality.**
  Example: If this situation makes me anxious, then I should avoid it.

- **"I must"/"I should": acting as if you have to force yourself or punish yourself to convince yourself to do something. This causes a great deal of guilt.**
  Example: I have to do all my housework tonight.

- **Labelling and mislabelling: applying a harsh, colourful, or emotionally loaded term to yourself or others.**
  Example: I'm stupid. He's lazy.

- **Personalization: holding yourself responsible for an unfortunate event that you alone are not actually responsible for.**
  Example: That date was not a success; it must be because of my weight.

Here is an example of a diary that can help you identify your thoughts, the emotions associated with them, and the cognitive distortions at play, and formulate alternative thinking:

Cognitive restructuring diary

DAY & TIME	CONTEXT	AUTOMATIC THOUGHT	EMOTION	COGNITIVE DISTORTION	ALTERNATIVE THOUGHT
Tuesday 8:00 p.m.	Alone in my kitchen	I ate a square of chocolate. I'm an idiot!	Shame Sadness Disappointment	Labelling All or nothing	I have the right to eat a delicious treat; it wasn't to manage a negative emotion. I ate it while savouring every bite. I enjoyed it. I'll binge less often if I allow myself treats from time to time.
Friday 7:00 p.m.	After a disappointing date, at a meeting place	He didn't want anything to do with me because I'm fat.	Anger Shame Rejection	Hasty conclusions	I didn't know why it didn't click for him; I can't know if he doesn't tell me. He saw my photo on my dating site profile. Just because I judge my body image harshly doesn't mean others do.

(continued on next page)

DAY & TIME	CONTEXT	AUTOMATIC THOUGHT	EMOTION	COGNITIVE DISTORTION	ALTERNATIVE THOUGHT
Sunday 11:00 a.m.	After a family brunch	I've binged again. I can't eat anything more all day.	Disgust Anger Guilt	All or nothing Exaggeration "I must"/ "I should"	Did my body need it because I didn't eat enough at brunch? Will eating too much at one meal make me gain weight? Holding myself back for the rest of the day might trigger another binge between now and this evening.
Monday 4:00 p.m.	My boss tells me I made a mistake	I hate my work. My boss doesn't understand anything. He's unfair to me.	Injustice Powerlessness Anger	Filtering Overgeneral-ization	Does a single negative comment represent my entire job? Do you have to be perfect at your job to enjoy it? Isn't it likely that other employees also get criticized for their work?
Wednesday 6:30 p.m.	While buying a bag of chips as I was leaving work	I worked hard all day without being able to stop to eat. I deserve this bag of chips.	Pride	"I must"/ "I should"	Does this work really require me to completely forgo my basic needs? Would taking 15 minutes to eat at work have made it easier for me to concentrate afterward?

DAY & TIME	CONTEXT	AUTOMATIC THOUGHT	EMOTION	COGNITIVE DISTORTION	ALTERNATIVE THOUGHT
Friday noon	My doctor tells me I have to lose weight	He thinks I am fat and lazy; I'll show him ... I'll eat if I want to.	Anger Shame Discouragement Humiliation	Emotional reasoning Jumping to conclusions	Is it possible that the doctor was tactless because of lack of time but that he was worried about my health? Bingeing just to show I'm right will punish only me; asserting myself with him would help more.
Friday 8:00 p.m.	An evening with no plans, no friends available	I feel so alone tonight; no one wants to be with me. The ice cream is calling to me from the fridge. I shouldn't ...	Loneliness Boredom Disappointment	"I must"/ "I should" All or nothing Personalization	All my friends had already made plans. It doesn't mean they don't want to be with me; it's bad timing. What could I do as an activity that I would enjoy and find distracting?

How to formulate an alternative thought

Once you've identified the cognitive distortions in your thoughts, it's time to formulate an alternative thought to modify the way you see things.

To come up with alternative thoughts, first question your thoughts or beliefs by confronting them with logical reasoning. For example:[2]

- What evidence am I relying on to say that?

- Why am I obliged to think or do that?

- Could there be other explanations?

- Am I inclined to exaggerate right now?

- Are my sources of information good?

- Am I replacing probabilities with certainties?

To create an alternative thought, you have to look for facts and not invent a positive thought you don't believe in. That would have absolutely no effect.

For instance, if you're stressed out over an exam and your partner tells you it will go fine, you will likely not be reassured. Whereas if they tell you it will go well because you've studied hard, and in the past when you studied hard, you got an excellent mark, it's highly likely your anxiety will decrease.

It's better to listen to the other (more rational) thoughts running through your head that are somewhat in the background but that you also believe in. Ask yourself, for example, what you would say to your best friend if they told you they had the same kind of thoughts.

How to manage intense negative emotions

Various techniques are effective in managing negative emotions. Here are some of them:

EXERCISE
Jacobson's relaxation technique

This relaxation exercise, certainly the best known in the Western world, is easy to do and effective. This is a shortened version:

1. Make yourself comfortable. This is your time!

2. Take five deep breaths, completely expelling the air from your abdomen each time, and imagine all the stressors you are thinking about leaving your body each time you breathe out.

3. Contract each of the following for 10 seconds and then relax each for 20 seconds, directing your thoughts to the feeling of relaxation and muscle

heaviness. Breathe normally as you contract and relax your muscles.

1.	Face	6.	Abdomen
2.	Fists	7.	Back
3.	Biceps	8.	Buttocks
4.	Neck	9.	Thighs
5.	Shoulders	10.	Feet

Finish the exercise by taking two deep breaths and directing your thoughts toward the overall feeling of relaxation in your body, like warmth radiating into each limb.

EXERCISE
Mindfulness within reach

For many of us, Jacobson's relaxation is not our cup of tea. However, in recent years another technique has gained popularity in the West: mindfulness meditation. Many people have learned to use and love this technique to manage their emotions and be more present in their daily lives.

Here's how to begin using mindfulness meditation:

1. Make yourself comfortable, sitting in an upright position, eyes closed.

2. Breathe deeply and pay attention to your breathing.

3. Feel all the parts of your body that participate in breathing.

4. Observe from a distance and let go of all the thoughts that pass through your mind, without judging.

5. Begin with 2 minutes each day and gradually increase the length of your sessions until you reach 10 to 15 minutes a session.

Several free apps such as Petit BamBou, Headspace, and Insight Timer provide short guided meditations. These can be a good place to start if your mind is overrun with anxieties.

A few tips for incorporating mindfulness into your routine

- When you wake up in the morning, place your hand on your abdomen and take five deep breaths.
- Notice your posture every time you sit down or stand up. Note the tension points and try to stretch.
- When you have a conversation, try to listen without judging or thinking about what you're going to say in response.
- When you go to bed, think about the day that has just ended and identify one thing you're grateful for.*

* M. Williams, J. Teasdale, A. Segal, and J. Kabat-Zinn, *The Mindful Way through Depression* (New York, Guilford Press), 2007.

EXERCISE
Wise Mind

The book *Dialectical Behavior Therapy for Binge Eating and Bulimia*[3] provides many tools for better managing emotions. One of the most interesting is called "Wise Mind." Its aim is to create a calm mental state.

Our mental state influences our thinking, our emotions, and the behaviours resulting from them. According to the authors, three main states of mind can be identified: Reasonable Mind, Emotion Mind, and Wise Mind.

Being in Reasonable Mind means we make decisions based on what is rational and logical. On the other hand, being in Emotion Mind implies that our decisions are controlled by our current emotions. In contrast, Wise Mind combines emotion and logic, resulting in a feeling of peace and well-being.

For example, when we buy a house, we may consider only Reasonable Mind (the least expensive house, the closest to work, etc.). We may also consider only Emotion Mind (the most beautiful house, the biggest, the most luxurious). Or we can choose to focus on Wise Mind (a house we feel comfortable in, where it's easy to imagine being happy and easy to imagine ourselves accomplishing all the activities and tasks of our current life without difficulty).

Wise Mind can be applied in many situations related to compulsive eating. Imagine that you've eaten normally all day but you leave the office very tired at the end of your workday. Emotion Mind encourages you to go on an eating binge to comfort yourself in the evening. Reasonable Mind instead recommends you go to bed and take care of yourself. Wise Mind offers an intuitive solution: enjoying a little bit of a food that gives you pleasure and then picking up a good book and going to bed when you're sleepy.

Wise Mind is the one that offers the best version of ourselves and encourages us to take care of ourselves. When we feel a desire to eat compulsively because of a powerful emotion, it's wise to recognize the desire, understand it, but not necessarily act on it. It's useful to observe and describe factually what we're experiencing, without making any judgment or comparison.

Choosing Wise Mind instead of Emotion Mind means that sometimes we'll make a decision that isn't the right one or isn't 100 percent satisfying but is one, on the other hand, that leaves us feeling calm, with fewer negative consequences to deal with later. Some authors[4] describe Wise Mind as a feeling close to intuition, with a physical sensation rooted in the gut, in the stomach area. This is in fact the most innervated part of the human body after the brain.

To try this experiment, answer these questions:

When you had your last episode of binge eating, what state of mind were you in? Reasonable, emotional, or wise?

If Wise Mind was not activated, how could you apply this mind the next time you feel like binge eating? How can you be more connected and aware of repercussions, without judging yourself?

_____

_____

_____

_____

_____

To put this technique into practice, it's recommended[5] that first you train yourself to observe and describe, in a detached way and without making judgments, the contexts in which you give in to binge eating (see the thoughts diary, page 36). Doing this enables your brain to break the link between feeling a desire to eat compulsively and acting on it. Think of this as a wave that rises and falls. Over time, and more and more often, you will manage to surf the wave, instead of being pulled under by it.

Remember that all waves subside sooner or later. Sometimes a desire can seem irresistible, and yet the more we train ourselves to watch it arrive, the faster the desire will pass. Learning to surf takes time, and it's normal to fall down while learning. What's important is to get back up and take a long-term view of your progress.

EXERCISE
The solution to the problem

Binge eating often becomes tempting when we feel overwhelmed by a situation or a problem. We need to consider how binge eating will solve the actual problem and realize it will have significant negative consequences. Once the emotion has lost some of its intensity and the cognitive distortions have been identified, we can consider applying a problem resolution technique to get a clearer picture.

Here are the steps to take:

1. Define the problem to be solved.

2. Identify all possible solutions.

3. Define the positive and negative consequences for each one.

4. Choose the solution with the most positive and the fewest negative consequences.

5. Apply it and reflect on the result.

Here's an example to familiarize you with its use:

Identify the problem to be solved	At university a member of my team has not completed his part of the work due in two days. I feel like an eating binge.
Define the problem to be solved	I might get a lower mark because this teammate has not done his work. That makes me anxious and angry.
Identify all possible solutions	1. Talk to the professor about the situation. 2. Do my teammate's work for him. 3. Go and meet with my teammate. 4. Binge eat.
Define the positive and negative consequences for each one	1. It's possible he won't help, but there is nothing to lose by asking him—he's a nice person. 2. That will take days and could jeopardize my other exam. This makes me feel angry again. 3. He'll be at class tonight; I can talk to him, but it could go badly. 4. I'll stop feeling anxious and angry temporarily, but the problem will still be there afterward. What's more, I'll feel guilty.
Choose the solution with the most positive and the fewest negative consequences	Plan A: #3 Plan B: #1
Apply it and reflect on the result	First of all, I have to speak to him to see if he can finish in time, then if not, speak to our professor. That went well. I'm proud of asserting myself. He apologized and will do the work tonight. It was a misunderstanding. I don't feel like bingeing any longer. I'll assert myself again in the future.

Now it's your turn:

Identify the problem to be solved	
Define the problem to be solved	
Identify all possible solutions	
Define the positive and negative consequences for each one	
Choose the solution with the most positive and the fewest negative consequences	
Apply it and reflect on the result	

Learning to assert yourself

Some of the most difficult challenges reported by our clients suffering from compulsive eating or binge eating disorder are receiving criticism, offering criticism, and managing to say no.

Have you ever been frustrated by a situation where you would have liked someone close to you to take care of you but you couldn't seem to ask the person directly? Have you felt angry because of the way someone treated you and you were not be able to set limits on their behaviour? You need to learn to assert yourself so you can take responsibility for achieving your own happiness, so you can help yourself, and so you can help others get to know themselves. Being able to state your needs and to define your limits in a respectful way helps build self-esteem.

Two important things to remember: Make sure you choose a time when the person you want to speak to is available and can listen to you. And make sure you understand what the other person is feeling, and you leave your judgments at the door. This means taking the time to listen, instead of passively waiting your turn to speak.

> ### Basic questions to ask yourself to ensure good communication
>
> I. Does my message clearly express what I feel?
> 2. Did the person I'm speaking to fully understand my message (should I check)?
> 3. Am I open to discussing and adjusting the difference in perception?

How to receive criticism

When you have low self-esteem, it can be hard to take criticism in a constructive way. Jean-Marie Boisvert and Madeleine Beaudry, in their excellent book *S'affirmer et communiquer—Asserting Yourself and Communicating*—describe several techniques for doing this. Here is an adaptation:

1. Listen without interrupting and with an open expression on your face.

2. Repeat the criticism to be sure you've understood it.

3. Explain your initial intention AND take responsibility for those parts of the criticism that are true.

4. Say what you're going to do to make things better in the future.

5. Don't play tennis! Wait for another occasion to criticize this person.

How to express criticism

Following a negative emotion, we sometimes have to voice criticism in order to have our limits respected. Here are key phrases to use in these situations:

- When you do this . . .

- I feel . . .

- Next time I would prefer that . . .

Example 1

When you interrupt me repeatedly . . .

- I feel like I'm not being listened to. I feel hurt.

- Next time I would prefer that you wait until I finish my sentences before giving me your opinion.

Example 2

When you make our holiday reservations without knowing whether the dates suit me . . .

- I feel like I don't count in our relationship and that makes me angry.

- Next time I would prefer that you wait for me to confirm that my boss has authorized my holidays before making any reservations.

Example 3

When you don't participate in the housework . . .

- I feel alone and discouraged.

- Next time I would prefer that you reserve some time so we can do our housework together on Sunday mornings.

Learning to say no

Whether it's at work or at home, saying no to demands seems to be very hard for most of our clients. "Why is it important to be able to turn down a request? I might be rejected," you'll say. Yet if we take the time to observe the process that follows the acceptance of an unwanted demand, we realize the risks are lower when we refuse. Think about it: Aren't you angry when you agree to do something you don't really want to do? How do you feel about the person who asked you to do it? Do you manage to complete the task as efficiently as you would have if you had respected your needs?

How to say no gradually to a demand

1. "I understand you would like such and such, but it doesn't suit me."

2. "I don't want you to keep insisting. I get the feeling you don't respect my decision."

3. "I'd like you to stop insisting."[6]

Modifying your thoughts and reactions is a lengthy process that doesn't happen overnight. Becoming aware of the emotions and thoughts that can trigger or accentuate your binge eating is already a big step forward. You may want to pursue this approach by joining a support group or with the help of a psychologist. You'll find a list of specialized resources in appendix 3 of this book.

Remember

✓ Food is not an effective, long-lasting solution for defusing negative emotions.

✓ Your emotions have a role to play. Learn to recognize them so you can use them to assert yourself.

✓ You can identify activities and techniques to reduce the intensity of your emotions and then tackle the real problem directly.

✓ Your thoughts are sometimes based on false beliefs that distort your perception of yourself and situations. It's possible to reexamine these automatic thoughts and replace them with more rational and constructive alternative thoughts.

CHAPTER

5

LISTENING TO HUNGER
AND FULLNESS CUES

We live in a society where abundance reigns. So it's not easy to listen to our hunger and fullness cues. Yet this is the basis of long-term weight control. By adopting an intuitive approach to food, you allow yourself to eat everything, as long as you pay attention to your actual hunger. But first, you have to be able to recognize what real hunger is.

Appetite, hunger, and fullness—What's the difference?

Appetite is what regulates the amount of energy required to meet the body's metabolic needs. It varies from person to person, depending on the conditions the person is exposed to. The processes that govern appetite operate naturally, but the lifestyle in developed countries sometimes seems to disrupt even these innate processes.

Hunger makes itself felt through physical symptoms such as a rumbling stomach, a drop in energy level, or a decrease in the ability to concentrate. These physical sensations tell you it's time to provide the body with some energy. Surrounded by a constant and copious supply of food (in supermarkets, convenience stores, restaurants, vending machines, etc.), we're often fooled by a feeling of *false hunger*, or psychological hunger: a desire to eat caused by the sight of a food or by its aroma, without real hunger!

Recognizing the feeling of hunger

Some physical signs of real hunger:
- My stomach is rumbling.
- I feel like I have an empty pit in my stomach.
- I feel weak; I lack energy.

Some examples of false hunger:
- I'm at a café and the aroma of a cinnamon bun makes me want to have one.
- I'm bored; I'm going to eat to keep myself busy.
- I'm at the checkout counter and I see a new flavour of chocolate bar I'd like to try.
- My boss brings in donuts every morning and I can't resist, even though I had a good breakfast at home.

A feeling of fullness tells us our appetite has been satisfied and we've eaten enough. When this feeling is acknowledged, we quickly realize that food suddenly holds less interest and has less flavour, and that the actual feeling of hunger has disappeared. But it's not always simple! Eating fast, on the run, or in front of the TV impairs our ability to pick up these signals, even though they're there.

10 tips for applying the intuitive approach

1. **Zero guilt!**
   The intuitive approach doesn't ban any food. This means
   you can treat yourself to a delicious pastry and not feel
   guilty. Guilt affects self-esteem and can lead to food cravings. Eat, enjoy it, and accept yourself as you are.

2. **Eat only when you really are hungry.**
   Although the intuitive approach allows you to eat anything, you must feel *real* hunger before you eat. Am I

really hungry, or do I just want to eat? This question isn't always easy to answer.

3. **Don't wait until you're too hungry before eating.**
If you wait until hunger sets in, you'll lose control more frequently and eat too much. Better to have a snack to avoid being too hungry at mealtimes. Refer to the 3–3–3 rule on page 30.

4. **Eat to satisfy your hunger, but no more.**
To stop in time, you have to eat slowly, put your fork down between mouthfuls, and take a few moments to savour your food. This way you recognize more easily when you have eaten enough and there's no need to clean your plate. The foods no longer taste as good? You're feeling satisfied? These are signs that you're full.

5. **Take pleasure in eating!**
For many people, eating has become an automatic activity and enjoyment isn't part of the process. Yet eating is one of the pleasures of life. You need to think of meals as precious moments for sharing, conversation, and culinary discovery.

6. **Get regular exercise.**
Studies show that getting regular physical activity helps us recognize hunger and fullness cues better. Another reason to get active.

7. **Get seven to nine hours of sleep every night.**
Sleep deprivation (six hours or less a night) is associated with an increased desire to eat (especially sweet foods) and has a negative impact on fullness signals. Sleeping more than nine hours a night can bring on symptoms of depression and result in a diet controlled by emotions. Try to get from seven to nine hours of sleep to better control your cravings.

8. **Trust yourself**
People who have tried many diets will have trouble letting go of food control. Learn to trust yourself, and hunger and fullness cues will become more and more obvious.

9. **Don't copy your neighbour.**
No one has the same needs and the same appetite. People who have an unhealthy relationship with food tend to imitate the people they're eating with. For instance: "My girlfriend didn't finish her plate. I'm going to do the same, or else she'll think I eat way too much." Eat to satisfy your own appetite, and if it tells you to clean your plate, then do it.

10. **Assert yourself with others.**
Your mother-in-law made you your favourite seafood lasagna and you're full after eating half your plateful. So as not to disappoint her, do you eat the entire plateful and even accept her offer to have just another little piece? Learn to assert yourself more. Say, for example, "Thanks, this lasagna is really delicious, but I'm not hungry anymore. I'd

love to take this piece for my lunch at work tomorrow." Similarly, if a work colleague offers you a piece of her coconut cake and you loathe that flavour, tell her so honestly.

EXERCISE
Eating mindfully

Intuitive eating is based on the approach used in mindful meditation. It involves immersing yourself in the moment and being attentive to all the sensations you experience as you eat. This little exercise will help you better understand intuitive eating:

Take one of your pleasure foods. It may be chocolate, ice cream, a croissant, whatever—a food you enjoy but that can cause a certain degree of anxiety when you eat it.

1. Settle into a quiet place you like.

2. Give yourself a normal serving of your pleasure food.

3. Take the time to appreciate its colour and visual appearance.

4. Put it into your mouth and describe the texture of this food. Melting, crunchy, crispy?

5. What flavours can you detect? Vanilla, hazelnut, butter? Does the taste linger in your mouth?

Tasting food using the intuitive method resembles the technique used for tasting wine (or even olive oil), wherein we describe a wine's colour, olfactory notes, flavours, and mouth feel. We do the same thing with food. Tasting this way involves all our senses and gives us pleasure. Anxiety-causing foods are seen in a new light and no longer bolted down at the kitchen counter or even in secret. They aren't considered forbidden anymore, and this is bound to improve food habits.

Reconnecting with your feelings of hunger and fullness

The success of the intuitive approach lies in listening to your hunger and fullness sensations. In a society where we have learned to clean our plates regardless of hunger, to eat sweets in ever larger portions, or simply to eat because it's mealtime, learning to recognize our food-related sensations is especially difficult. Our parents even told us we had to clean our plates to get dessert! Fortunately, approaches have changed, and nowadays parents are taught to respect their children's needs, since they're the ones who actually know when they've had enough.

There's nothing like a food diary to monitor whether you're paying attention to your feelings. Start to keep a diary tomorrow describing not only what you eat but also your hunger level before, and your fullness level after, the meal or snack. This exercise pays off!

Food diary

Sylvie's example

TIME	HUNGER LEVEL (0–5)	MENU	FULLNESS LEVEL (0–5)	REFLECTION
7:00 a.m.	4	1 small orange juice 1 piece of toast with butter 1 coffee with milk and sugar	2	I'm still hungry, but I'm in a hurry; I have to leave for work.
10:00 a.m.	5	1 large muffin 2 servings of butter 1 coffee with milk and sugar	5	I feel like I ate too much too fast.
12:30 p.m.	1	1 ham sandwich 1 V8 juice 3 chocolate chip cookies	5	I realize the cookies were too much. I eat them out of habit every lunchtime because I like a little something sweet, but today I'm really too full.

TIME	HUNGER LEVEL (0–5)	MENU	FULLNESS LEVEL (0–5)	REFLECTION
6:00 p.m.	3	I large bowl of pasta with rosé sauce I slice of bread with butter steamed broccoli I glass of wine 2 low-fat yogurts	5	I don't like broccoli, but I force myself because it's good for my health. I would have liked a bowl of ice cream for dessert, but I took the low-calorie option. I ate two out of frustration!
8:30 p.m.	0	I bag of chips shared between two people	5	I'm in the habit of eating in front of the TV; deep down, I knew I wasn't hungry, but it's my little moment of comfort at the end of the day. I enjoy eating something crunchy.

This diary tells us that Sylvie doesn't pay much attention to her hunger sensations. Since she was still hungry after breakfast, she should have taken a snack with her to eat when she got to work (crackers and cheese, for instance). This snack may have replaced the mid-morning muffin. At noon the cookies could have been replaced, since Sylvie did not really want them. The yogurt could probably have been fitted in at noon. And in the evening Sylvie would have been more satisfied had she eaten something she enjoyed for dessert (if she was still hungry, of course). Because she didn't satisfy her real want (a bowl of ice cream), she ate a double serving of low-fat yogurt, which isn't much better. As for the broccoli, it could easily have been replaced by a vegetable she prefers—maybe a carrot salad, or sautéed peppers, or a spinach-and-almond salad.

It's easy to associate watching TV with eating—but hard to pay attention to our fullness cues when we eat while watching TV. You've undoubtedly had the experience of eating while watching a program and suddenly realizing you're holding an empty bowl, then wondering where the food you just served yourself went. Keep your hands busy to break this association. Knit. Draw. When you're hungry, take a break from the TV, sit down at the table, and savour what you're eating.

Remember

✓ Intuitive eating is the key to rediscovering the pleasure in eating.

✓ Mindful eating is a total sensory experience that leads to a better relationship with food.

✓ Respecting your hunger and fullness signals is essential in any approach aiming to improve your eating behaviour.

✓ Keeping a food diary to take note of your hunger and fullness sensations is an effective awareness-building tool.

CHAPTER

6

LIFESTYLE, A SAFETY NET

In addition to making dietary changes and modifying automatic thoughts, changes in lifestyle can also improve our relationship with foods. Complementary strategies include sleeping well, getting regular physical activity, and managing stress.

To sleep or not to sleep?

While sleeping is in itself a fairly passive activity, it's essential to many physiological processes and contributes especially to healthy weight control.

Sleep helps regulate the production of *leptin* and *ghrelin*, two hormones that influence appetite. A lack of sleep decreases the level of leptin, the hormone that reduces appetite (also called the fullness hormone), and increases the level of ghrelin, the hormone that stimulates appetite. When we sleep less, we're more likely to feel hungrier, overeat, and gain weight. Long sleepers (9.5 or 10 hours a night or more) are also affected by this hormonal disruption. Seven to nine hours of sleep a night is recommended.

Tips for sleeping well

√ Avoid eating a meal too high in protein in the evening. Instead, choose fish and vegetable proteins, rather than that big piece of red meat.

✓ Always have grain products or a starch (potato, sweet potato) in the evening to maximize serotonin levels.

✓ Avoid large, high-fat meals in the evening. They slow down digestion too much.

✓ Watch caffeine and alcohol intake—they can interfere with good sleep. Caffeine stimulates the nervous system and inhibits melatonin secretion. Alcohol decreases the amount of deep sleep, the most restorative phase.

True or false?

It's best to avoid alcohol in any form.

False

Alcohol consumption is a personal choice. In moderate amounts, it can be a perfectly normal part of a balanced diet. On the other hand, it does have depressant and disinhibiting effects. Alcohol consumption may thus increase the risk of binge eating, as well as the risk of experiencing negative emotions. In social situations, drinking a substitute like sparkling water, apple cider, or dealcoholized beer can help you feel you're taking part in the fun—without having to pay a price later.

✓ Get regular physical activity. Avoid intense training in the evening if it disrupts sleep.

✓ Establish a stable sleep schedule. Make a point of getting up at the same time, even on weekends. If you go to bed late one night, go to bed earlier the next night, as soon as you start to feel tired. Avoid afternoon naps, if possible; or limit them to less than 45 minutes.

✓ If you can't get to sleep, avoid thoughts like "I have to sleep, otherwise I'll never get through my day!" since anxiety is incompatible with the relaxation that precedes sleep.

✓ Listen to your body: when you start to yawn and your eyelids feel heavy, it's time to go to bed. It's useless to set a fixed bedtime (only a fixed rising time); your body will let you know when it's tired.

✓ Establish a sleep routine your brain will recognize in the evening. For example, if most of the time you notice that you begin to yawn around 10 o'clock, then at 9 get into your pyjamas, brush your teeth, lower the lights, and do something calming like reading a book.

✓ Avoid screens (TV, computer, tablet, reader, smartphone) for at least an hour before going to bed, and never use them during the night. The brain interprets the white light of these devices as daylight.

✓ Use your bed only for sleeping and sex. Avoid working in bed, so as not to create a bed-work association.

✓ Leave a notepad with a pencil and a soft light on your bedside table. During the night, if work-related thoughts occur (for example, "I'm afraid I'll forget to copy that document tomorrow"), write them down quickly. Then turn your thoughts toward the relief you feel: "That's done—I won't forget about it—I can concentrate on my very comfortable bed."

✓ If you wake up and have trouble getting back to sleep, leave the bedroom to read a novel (print version!). Watch for signs of drowsiness (yawns, heavy eyelids), and when they occur, go back to bed.

Exercising to feel better

We all know that physical activity is good for overall health. What's less well known is that it generates *endorphins*, neurotransmitters with a positive effect on stress and anxiety management, the quality of sleep, and mood. Exercising outdoors seems to be especially effective.

Studies have measured the effects of physical activity in people with binge eating disorder. Aerobics and yoga have reduced the number of attacks and the weight of people who binge eat. Doing aerobic activities has also lessened symptoms of depression.

There's no need to start an exhausting program. Walking is fine and can be done regardless of physical condition. Why not set yourself the goal of getting out for 15 minutes a day, just for a breath of fresh air?

Exercise has many benefits—for physical *and* mental health. Avoid exercising to burn calories—do it just to feel better.

5 tips for getting more exercise

1. **Find a physical activity you like.**
   If you hate gyms, don't bother with them. To have an active lifestyle, find an activity you like. Dance or swimming classes; or a walking or tennis club; or exercise videos on YouTube or on DVDs you buy at a store, for instance.

2. **Exercise as a family or with friends.**
   It's always more motivating to engage in a physical activity with a partner or your family. Skating, tobogganing, playing ball—any activity is a good opportunity to get out and get some air.

3. **Hire a trainer.**
   This is often a good way to get motivated, especially at the beginning, and to set up a personalized plan that takes into account your physical limits or pain.

4. **Establish a realistic goal.**
You don't need to run a marathon to reap the benefits of fitness training. Why not make a list of more achievable goals? Start by walking 10 minutes a day, then introduce 30-second blocks of slow running, for example. As the weeks go by, increase the length of your fitness sessions.

5. **Record your progress.**
It's motivating to record physical fitness progress. Such as: You're no longer breathless when you climb stairs. Or, your flexibility has improved. Or, you're sleeping better. Results like these make you want to continue.

Ah, the joys of stress!

There are many sources of stress: The need to perform well in the workplace. A lack of financial resources. Illness. Family conflicts. Many people have physical symptoms as a consequence: stomach aches, nausea, reflux.

Did you know that stress can also influence our appetite? In periods of stress, *cortisol,* a hormone that enables us to react to danger, mobilizes energy from sugars and sends it where it's needed most in the body. When there is a cortisol imbalance, cravings for both fatty and sweet foods—comfort foods—occur. Although this phenomenon isn't yet completely understood, it appears that eating fatty foods stimulates the brain's pleasure centres. And sweet foods, as we saw in chapter 2, contribute to the production of serotonin, the neurotransmitter associated with a feeling of well-being.

Strategies for limiting stress-related cravings

- **Include grain products or equivalents (sweet potato, potato, quinoa) in every meal.**
  Getting enough carbohydrate increases the serotonin level in the blood.

- **Brush your teeth carefully.**
  Brushing your teeth carefully and then using dental floss is often effective. Try it and you'll see: it's easier to resist the temptation to eat again afterward.

- **Chew gum.**
  Chewing a piece of gum (careful—not the entire pack!) is a trick made popular by people trying to stop smoking. Chewing on something also often takes your attention away from food.

- **Drink some herbal tea or regular tea.**
  Having a cup of herbal tea or regular tea makes for a little break. Having a hot drink relaxes you naturally. Some herbal teas even have relaxing properties (chamomile, verbena).

- **Keep busy and relax!**
  Finding an alternative activity when stress makes you want to eat is always a winning strategy. Why not use it to your advantage by calling a friend, going for a walk, or doing a breathing exercise?

EXERCISE
An anti-stress tool: visualization

Here's an effective technique[1] for increasing your stress tolerance:

- Choose a safe and relaxing place. It can be real or imaginary and it doesn't have to be far away; for some people, it's their bedroom; for others, their parents' home. If coming up with a place is difficult, you can also choose a calming colour.

- Take a deep breath in through the nose while inflating your abdomen, hold your breath for five seconds, and then breathe out through your mouth. Repeat three times and then breathe quietly for the remainder of the visualization.

- With your eyes closed, imagine arriving in your safe place. Describe it with your five senses: Is it hot or cold? Is there sunshine that warms you and bathes your body? What do you hear? What colours do you see around you? What's the surface under your feet?

- As you move forward, what can your hands touch that is reassuring? Is there a soothing smell? Can you taste a delicious food? Choose a calming element to focus your attention on and stay in this place for a few minutes.

- Recognize how safe and relaxed you feel. Focus on your breathing and open your eyes when you're ready.

Remember

✓ Modifying your lifestyle habits will make your relationship with food more harmonious.
✓ Sleeping better, getting more exercise, and managing stress better make it easier to regain your equilibrium.

LEARNING TO LIKE
YOUR BODY IMAGE

The perception we have of ourselves and our bodies is often coloured by beliefs and emotions. It's seldom objective. For example, we've all known people who call themselves "fat" even though they're at a normal weight. And we certainly know people who are overweight and feel good about their bodies the way they are. Why is this?

First, it's important to distinguish between body image and actual physical appearance. It's possible to have an objectively healthy or attractive physical appearance and have a very bad body image. The opposite is also possible. Body image is shaped by many external factors and reflects the society we live in.

> *"When Isabelle asked me to write about body diversity, I wanted to speak to you directly. Be honest: Did you start your day by looking at yourself in the mirror? Did you climb onto the scale? If so, tell me: What emotions did you feel at that moment?*
>
> *All of us, women and men, have our own relationship with our image. I hope yours is healthy and balanced. Often, it's when we make comparisons that things get complicated. If we compare ourselves with what we see on TV, in the movies, in magazines, in stores, on models, or on the web, we may feel that the image in our mirror is ugly or inadequate. We're*

too hard on ourselves! Never forget that those images are retouched, arranged, polished, and unreal. That ideal of beauty does not exist. There isn't just one mould for the human body. There are billions. My shape has changed in recent years. That's life. My life. But I feel beautiful because I have lots of energy and good health. That's what I work on. I make sure to keep in shape and get enough sleep; I aim for balance, and I can tell you that I pretty much achieve it. I have defined my beauty. I smile at life. I accept challenges with courage and energy. My eyes shine with happiness because I live a fulfilling life. And when I see myself in the mirror or on TV, I say to myself, 'You're alive! So go for it!' I hope you will think this way, too."

Best regards,
Ève-Marie Lortie, TV host

Co-president of La CHIC, La Charte québécoise pour une image corporelle saine et diversifiée (Quebec Charter for a Healthy and Diverse Body Image)

jesigneenligne.com

The media and society's expectations of women

Most of our female clients feel that society expects them to be thinner, more athletic, and more feminine. Part of this pressure is internal, since women are often their own most critical judge. The kind of body image we acquired as children is also a factor. Did the women around you talk in a disparaging way about their own bodies? Was the physical appearance of girls more important than that of boys? Were you encouraged to fall in line with common stereotypes like playing with Barbie dolls and pretending to be a princess? Without doubt, over time these sexist models shape our perception of beauty.

However, another part of this pressure is external and very real. Everywhere you look, magazines, TV, movies, and ads display highly stereotyped models of women. Few women identify with the models on billboards, and being slightly overweight poses no health risk whatsoever, yet the general public readily criticizes people who don't correspond to cultural standards of thinness. We encourage you to develop a critical attitude and question the ideals of beauty presented in the media.*

The ideals of beauty and weight seen everywhere put enormous pressure on girls. Since our control over our weight and physical appearance is limited, getting caught up in this quest for perfection is dangerous. When you compare yourself with a girlfriend, don't forget that each of us has a unique

---

* We encourage you to watch the videos *Body Evolution—Model Before and After* and *Dove Evolution* on YouTube to develop a critical eye for ads.

genetic heritage. Your friend might have a naturally low body weight, whereas you might develop an eating disorder in an effort to weigh the same. Is the sacrifice worth it? If being happy means being the thinnest or most beautiful person in the room, you're guaranteed disappointment. There will always be something that someone else has "more of," so it's important to base our self-esteem on characteristics that make us unique.

The same thinking applies to cosmetic surgery. "I'll just get one thing fixed and after that I'll be perfect." But the obsession seldom stops there, and thus begins an infinite spiral of physical changes to achieve a social norm of perfection. The satisfaction is temporary and our concern then moves on to something else. And what happens when we begin to get older?

Instead, why not put the emphasis on our body's functioning, which we often forget to do, rather than on its appearance? What does your body allow you to do? Are you grateful to it?

It's also important to change our models of comparison. Why not choose models of beauty that include people with a less conventional body image? This allows us to see that beauty is not directly related to thinness. Let's be kind to one another by paying attention to our own inner narrative and, in doing so, generate compassion and acceptance for ourselves and for others.

EXERCISE
Different models

1. Think of women you admire who have a less conventional body image.

2. What do you most admire about these women?

And what about men?

According to a study conducted over many years,[1] in 1997, 43 percent of men reported being dissatisfied with their overall appearance, whereas in 1972 this figure was just 15 percent. We see this in clinical practice, as well: our male clients tell us they feel more and more pressure to look like a muscled, hairless Adonis. In an era when CrossFit is in fashion, many men tell us that the obsession with muscles, virility, and healthfulness is becoming overwhelming. This makes it important to change our perception of eating disorders, since for one thing men seek help less often and less quickly. Ring the alarm bell if a man you know continues to train in spite of injuries, if his self-esteem is based solely on his body image, or if his interpersonal relationships begin to suffer because of the way he eats or how often he trains.

"I've gone from one eating disorder to another over the years. Right now I'm in remission, and I stay there by observing my behaviour, both when things are fine and when they're not going so well. I've had binge eating episodes in the past. I have a sweet tooth, so my attacks involved cookies, chocolate, etc. Sometimes I'd start eating one, then two rows of cookies, and before I knew it, I'd reached the bottom of the package! While I was at it, I'd follow up with ice cream. I'd emerge from this round of bingeing feeling like a coke addict who'd cheated on his wife after using. I saw just how bad the damage was. I punished myself and I felt guilty. Repeating it is what caused the most pain. Before, I used to tune out; now, I'm aware of what's going on.

How did I get into remission? First, I learned to recognize the signals that I was about to go off the rails food-wise. It's easy to look at the fridge and be tempted to eat to deal with a problem that's bothering you. Meditation taught me to observe my mind: 'Why did I go into the fridge?' I eat my pleasure food and suddenly I need more. I stop myself. 'But what am I doing here?' I ask myself, 'Do I want to feel the way I do after an attack?' I forestall the attack by being aware of my actions. I've succeeded, by training my mind, in being present, in disconnecting from the attack. I ride my horse and not the other way around. I'm more powerful mentally, even though my horse has more physical strength. I control the attack, not the opposite. I'm able to see the negative consequences of losing control. It's just like cheating on your spouse or taking drugs; when you're aware of what you're doing and conscious of the consequences and the bad things that lie in wait for you, you lose the taste for it.

If I realize that what's bothering me is a financial worry or being rejected by a girl, for example, I name the emotion that's causing me pain and I talk about it openly with people I care about. I analyze my behaviour, thoughts, and fantasies. I can't stand being unhappy. I need to talk about what's happening to me. I laugh at myself and downplay the situation. Words are my painkillers! For me, talking is a lifesaver. I feel recognized and accepted; even if it's a lot of emotional nonsense and a big load of emotions, I feel relieved. Learning to live with the fragility of an eating disorder becomes less serious; it's not a prison sentence. As the adage says so well: One day at a time . . . I accept today for what it is, and I make the most of present moments. I become a witness to what's happening to me. I don't take myself too seriously. I find where the emotion is in my body and I welcome it. I agree to let the pain be, to be comfortable with discomfort.

I'm condemned to be happy; I don't have any choice about being happy—I know too well what it is to want to die. Every single day I have to look after myself. I have to exercise, meditate, do things I enjoy to be happy. The more I look after myself, the more my happiness is the backdrop to my life. I'm the *captain of my ship. I know when my boat is listing, and I fix things as I go along.*

Something else that has really helped me is that every day I choose to put something into my mouth that I enjoy; I eat one or two pieces of dark chocolate and have an espresso and I savour them. It's a ritual. I break up my piece of chocolate and I let it melt. I love myself enough to spoil myself. I now spoil myself with my pleasure food, just as much as I used to punish myself. No need to go off the rails, since I know that every day I can have my pleasure food. Like exercising—every time I go kayaking, it's with a smile, not to punish myself for having eaten. Even if I've eaten more the day before, I'm not going to beat myself up.

In the winter I exercise less, and that's okay. I weigh myself more often during this period and I'm able to love myself, to let myself love myself at this weight and not hide myself when I take my clothes off. Being in good health is important so I can live a long life. This is at the centre of my life. I'll enjoy life just as much with a 10-pound difference in weight. Being really overweight would keep me from doing everything I want in my life. I'm looking for balance through kindness, gentleness, and compassion.

I'm in remission because I'm fully present, whether things are going well or not; whether the news is good or bad, I'm aware of myself."

—Jean-Marie Lapointe
In an interview with Dr. Catherine Senécal

We regularly hear from our new clients that they're afraid that if they become less obsessed with their weight, if they stop making themselves feel bad by insulting themselves and making themselves feel guilty about it, they will become or remain obese. Yet several studies on self-compassion show surprising results. For instance, one study[2] discovered that participants with binge eating disorder saw a considerable decrease in the frequency of their binge eating attacks when they applied self-compassion techniques. These techniques included, for example, psycho-education on the ineffectiveness of self-blaming, and visualization exercises on the theme of compassion. In other words, you don't have to beat yourself up to get results! Showing compassion toward ourselves makes it even easier to achieve our objectives. So why shouldn't you, too, have the right to a little bit of kindness?

EXERCISE
Developing compassion for yourself

1. Imagine a version of yourself as a child. This child tells you they're feeling fat today. What would you say to them? Would you be critical and dismissive with this child you love? How would you speak to them to motivate them with love and compassion?

_____

_____

_____

What five parts of your body do you currently like?

1. _____

2. _____

3. _____

4. _____

5. _____

3. How could you emphasize them more?

_____

_____

_____

_____

_____

Challenges to overcome

1. The next time someone pays you a compliment, instead of downplaying it or denying it, just say, "Thank you, that's very kind of you."

2. Try to stop doing things to check up on your body for seven days! Try not to pinch the chubbier parts of your body, and instead touch yourself as you would a friend. When you look in the mirror, don't just examine the body parts you like less; look at yourself as you would at a friend, as a whole. And wear clothes that fit you! For heaven's sake, let's stop the torture of wearing clothes that are too small, believing one day they will fit.

EXERCISE
The spheres of life

The spheres of life exercise[3] aims to diversify the areas of interest in the life of a person with an eating disorder. Obviously, the more your life is centred on just one thing, the more eggs you have put in one basket. If, for example, your life looks like the one depicted in the following graph, it's very likely that on a day when you feel less physically attractive, it will be devastating, since your self-esteem depends mainly on your body image and weight.

Spheres of life of people with an eating disorder

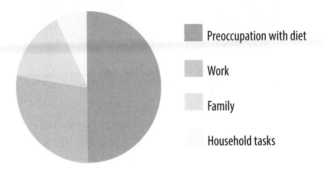

- ■ Preoccupation with diet
- ■ Work
- ■ Family
- Household tasks

Whereas if your life resembles the graph that follows, when you have a day where your body image is not as good, you have several other areas to draw your self-esteem from.

Spheres of life of people without an eating disorder

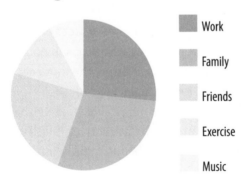

- ■ Work
- ■ Family
- Friends
- Exercise
- Music

What activities could you incorporate into your life to boost your self-esteem?

_____

_____

_____

What activities would help you experience pleasant physical sensations?

_____

_____

_____

_____

Sexuality and eating habits

More than 30 percent of people suffering from binge eating disorder say that they were sexually abused in childhood.[4] We've often seen female clients put on weight to hide their feminine curves, so as to blend in to the crowd and avoid attracting attention. Having men look at you when you've experienced sexual abuse can be hard to cope with.

On the other hand, how many married women admit to holding on to extra weight that they are unable to lose because it serves as a defense mechanism against attracting the attention of men and against their own temptations to be unfaithful?

Ask yourself:

- Is there a specific weight that represents a psychological barrier for you?

- Do you try to avoid having a sex life so as not to be in touch with the pain you once felt?

If this is the case, you need to deal with the problems and get help in doing so.

Coming to terms with your body image: promising paths forward

Therapeutic exposure to mirrors

Recent studies[5] take a new approach to working on the body image of clients with eating disorders. Since most people who don't like their body tend to avoid looking at it or, on the contrary, examine it compulsively, an exposure technique has been developed to encourage a more accurate view of the body by describing it without judgment, in an objective way.

EXERCISE
Observing yourself in a neutral way

This technique, used within a therapeutic framework, consists of describing yourself in front of a full-length mirror in judgment-free language, while paying no attention to the positive and negative emotions the exercise causes.

Six categories can be used to describe our bodies in a neutral way: outline, shape, colour, shading, texture, and function.

Want to try it?

Start with, for instance, a slightly shrivelled piece of fruit. Describe it completely, non-judgmentally: "I see a dark-orange-coloured globe. The texture is . . ."

Then begin to notice all the times you avoid the mirror or check on your body in a week. For example, when you pinch the fattest parts of your body . . .

Next, do the description exercise in front of a mirror, wearing a comfortable outfit. For example, begin your description this way: "I see a flesh-coloured oval sitting on top of a cylinder that is also flesh-coloured and a little narrower than the oval. On top of the oval, long brown threads hang down on each side . . ." And so on. Take the time to find truly neutral terms. It's normal for this to be hard. Each time you use new terms to describe yourself, new pathways form in your brain and the conditioning of your thoughts about your body begins to change.

Massage therapy

Massage therapy has a positive effect on curing eating disorders.[6] It helps lower the cortisol frequently associated with stress and increase the serotonin and dopamine that play an important role in managing eating behaviours. Subjects with an eating disorder have also reported gaining a better perception of their body image after several sessions of massage therapy.

Many clients have told us they avoid touching their bodies, and that when they do, they touch themselves roughly and quickly. A pleasant touch sends a message of unconditional body acceptance: "I deserve to feel pleasant sensations, no matter what my weight." Have you ever tried to apply cream to your body gently? This is one way to begin experiencing the pleasant sensations you can give your body.

Art therapy

Both adults and children communicate more easily through images than words.[7] Art therapy can allow you to express yourself on a theme such as your body or certain emotions, like anger, sorrow, or hope. You don't have to be Picasso. You can paint in watercolours, draw with a pencil, or make collages, for example.

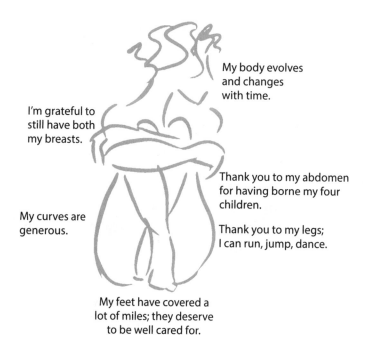

My body evolves and changes with time.

I'm grateful to still have both my breasts.

Thank you to my abdomen for having borne my four children.

My curves are generous.

Thank you to my legs; I can run, jump, dance.

My feet have covered a lot of miles; they deserve to be well cared for.

Physical exercise and yoga

One recent study[8] has shown the benefits of yoga on body image. Participants had a better body image and showed less objectification (the feeling of being reduced to a sexual object) when they practised yoga, no matter what kind.

Regardless of the type of exercise they do, our clients notice a positive impact on their moods and a better body image. What's important is to choose an activity that suits your preferences and one in which your weight does not affect your performance—an activity that realistically fits into your schedule and is enjoyable enough for you to invest your time in throughout your life, even if it has no effect on your weight.

Helping our children feel good about their body image

When body image is a hard thing for us to manage in our daily lives, we may sometimes wonder what to do to protect our children from having these complexes. A few tips to guide your thinking follow.

7 tips to help your children develop a good body image

1. Discuss beauty as perceived in various cultures; show them photos of diverse eras and cultures.

2. Ask them what they like best about their bodies.

3. Ask them which parts of their bodies reflect their family and cultural heritage: "I have the same nose as Daddy and Grandpa!"

4. Encourage them to take a critical approach to the media and the body images they present.

5. Ask your children not to compare their bodies with their friends'; remind them that each body is unique and that we have little control over our genetic inheritance.

6. Encourage them to play a sport not with the aim of losing weight but just to feel good about themselves and have fun.

7. Discuss with your pubescent children the changes they're seeing in their bodies; validate the fact that such changes are normal, and talk openly about sexuality as a beautiful and good thing.

How can I keep from passing on an eating disorder to my child?

Many parents with concerns about their bodies and their weight displace these behaviours onto their children. We often see teenagers who tell us they were put on a diet by a parent as early as age 10. You now know that strict diets do not work for adults; this is also true for children. Furthermore, this approach teaches children that their bodies are not acceptable the way they are. In order not to pass on our own concerns, we need to educate ourselves about the problem and prevent it indirectly.

At home you can emphasize, through cooking and eating together, the enjoyment food provides. Despite the fast-paced lives we now lead, making it a priority to eat as a family as we engage in light conversation creates a positive association with food. Unless there is a particular problem (a medical condition), your children should rely on their hunger to know when to stop eating. They will also learn by imitation, so if you belittle your own body or openly judge those of others, they will do the same with theirs.

At school you can get involved in opposing weigh-ins in physical education classes. Weigh-ins increase preoccupation with weight and stigmatize children with a body that is outside the norm. You can also encourage your children to think critically by asking them about the gender-stereotyped activities they're involved in. Do the girls do ballet and gymnastics and the boys play hockey? Why not suggest a soccer team to your daughter or perhaps not let her use makeup before a certain age.

5 tips to ensure your children develop a healthy relationship with food

1. Eliminate all comments about weight, calories, or other nutritional concepts, and comments like "I don't serve starches; they make you fat."

2. At mealtimes tell your children to listen to what their stomach is saying. Is it telling them it's still hungry? Is it saying they've had too much?

3. Show them how to cook with enjoyment; teach them family recipes.

4. Eat as a family while conversing at the table, without TV.

5. Make eating an enjoyable activity. Go and meet vegetable producers as a family or plant your own garden.

"I'm the product of 'broken' parents, each struggling with various unresolved issues, ranging from fear of abandonment to self-medicated anxiety. It was no surprise that the marriage ended in a bitter divorce when I was four years old.

My mother was remarkably beautiful but saw countless flaws in the mirror. Even though she often told us, my sister and me, that we were fantastic, she frequently made comments about our physical appearance.

I learned that, according to my mother, women should have straight legs, white teeth, shiny hair, fair skin, and physical proportions appropriately distributed. I didn't correspond to this ideal—like 90 percent of society. My father was disparaging of my mother and never missed an opportunity to make degrading comments about her. Because of his constant criticisms, I felt like a second-rate person when I visited him with his new wife and 'perfect' children.

These imperfect parents imposed extremely high standards on us. Crispy bacon had to be eaten with a knife and fork. Children were to be seen but not heard. *I remember the time we had forgotten to take our skates when we went to spend Christmas with our father, and as a punishment, we spent hours in the biting cold watching his wife's children skate in their winter clothes. All we had were light coats, polyester pants, and leather boots. It was torture. We could never express dissatisfaction about unacceptable treatment. My mother and father often told me, 'If you aren't happy, you can go and live with your father/mother.' And 'It's this or nothing.' And 'I'm still your mother/father.' I stopped thinking about my needs and concentrated on what was required of me. I learned to tolerate the intolerable. Food was a good distraction, a comfort, and in large amounts it could soothe almost any pain. It filled a void I was already feeling but hadn't yet identified.*

When I turned seven, my well-intentioned mother began to take me to see nutritionists, hypnotherapists, and doctors to help me manage a non-existent weight problem. Both my parents sent contradictory messages, blaming us when we ate too much, but also when we didn't clean our plates. I was rewarded with ice cream when I avoided sweets during one of my many diets. I was given popcorn and other treats so I would watch movies with my mother instead of playing outside. I soon lost my bearings. Every meal came with an enormous serving of anxiety. The meals I ate in public . . .

At 16 I had a part-time job and a driver's licence. I started to patronize the drive-through at various restaurants and find dark parking places where I could eat large amounts of food. I bought two drinks to make the employees think I was ordering for more than one person. Sometimes I went to more than one restaurant, making sure to hide the remains of my previous meal under the seat of my mother's car. Obviously I disposed of this evidence before going home, the windows down to get rid of the smell of the food. When I came back and parked the car, it was as if nothing had happened. I alone knew the secret and bore the guilt. Food helped me forget the shame, the emptiness, and the guilt . . . temporarily.

In my twenties, with a full-time salary, an apartment, and my own car, my binge eating reached its peak. I usually ate my first meal at noon. Several hours before the end of my workday, I began obsessively planning my next binge. I stopped at a drive-through to buy something to eat on my way to the Chinese restaurant. There, I ordered 12 spring rolls and a family-size box of sweet-and-sour chicken balls, imagining the employees would think I was having friends for dinner. I don't know why that was important to me, but it was. I ate alone in front of the television until I felt stuffed. Then I drank diet soda until I could eat again. By bedtime the entire order had disappeared. I slept like a baby until the next day, when I woke up disgusted with myself and empty. Always empty.

It's been 17 years since my first call for help. I can confirm with certainty that I've tried everything to break the compulsive cycle, including psychological and pharmaceutical therapy. I've lost and regained hundreds of pounds with diets and exercise programs, and I've even attended Overeaters Anonymous meetings. Following doctors' advice, I had a longitudinal gastrectomy. I hoped that the fact of being physically unable to eat would help me. And it worked, but it wasn't a miracle cure. A year after the surgery, I had begun to put weight back on.

A number of therapists and nutritionists have helped me make significant changes over the years. The most arduous task has been to reconcile myself with my past and forgive my parents for their failings. I've come to accept that my broken parents were quite simply unable to give me the care I needed. I've chosen to believe they loved me to the best of their abilities and to hang on to the good memories I have of them. I see them as being like paraplegic parents who can't run in the park with their children. I can't resent them for their inadequacies, even though these did me harm. I try to view them as broken but well-intentioned, which I sincerely believe is the case.

Another Herculean task has been to learn to assert myself. I was so used to saying yes to everybody that I had never asked myself what I wanted. "What do I want?" is a question I have to ask myself several times a day. It's a foreign concept to me. My instincts had always compelled me to answer what I believed others wanted to hear. Knowing what I want is a big help . . . However, the object of the exercise is to ask the question. Communicating my needs to others

remains a challenge, especially when it involves bro-
ken individuals close to me. I've worked to develop
this ability, with the help of my therapists. I've had
to let my friends and family know what my limits
are. I've begun to feel less guilty when asked to take a
friend's place. I wouldn't hold it against anybody else
if they asked me for what they need, so why would I
feel guilty about doing the same?

With time I felt less and less empty. The more
I looked after my emotional needs, the less binge
eating I did. A nutritionist convinced me to aban-
don all the food rules I had put in place through
the years. I decided to eat what I wanted, even if
it wasn't what I 'should' eat. It wasn't easy for me,
someone who followed the rules and liked to please
people, to turn my back on the diet industry so as
to better listen to my internal voice. I try to eat
for enjoyment to the point where I am comfortably
satisfied, and I try to stop before becoming uncom-
fortably full. I accept the fact that my plate may
still contain food when my body tells me I've had
enough. I take home the leftovers to relieve the anx-
iety associated with leaving food on my plate. At
other times I order a first course instead of a full
meal, with the option of ordering something else if
I'm still hungry. I have permission to be hungry and
eat more. I note my food preferences. I buy the may-
onnaise whose taste I prefer. I tell myself I have the
right to eat and I deserve to take pleasure in eating.
I have this permission because I give it to myself.

I still have eating binges, but less often. When I'm alone in the car, I feel like going to the drive-through. Then I ask myself, 'What do I want?' Sometimes I go home. Other times I buy fast food. But I no longer eat in the dark. And I try to listen to my feeling of fullness.

I'm trying to care for the seven-year-old child who couldn't defend herself. I've moved heaven and earth to look after others, and now I'm trying to turn these efforts inward, and I'm doing all I can so that little girl will feel loved, deserving, and fulfilled."

—*Annick*

Remember

✓ Having compassion for yourself does not mean you will become or remain overweight.

✓ Your body image may not reflect your actual physical appearance.

✓ Doing activities where you feel good about yourself for something other than your physical appearance or your weight will help you have a better relationship with your body and greater self-esteem.

✓ Body image develops in childhood, so be attentive around your children; avoid any remarks on the subject of weight and all comparisons with anyone else.

CHAPTER

SOS!
I NEED MORE HELP

This chapter is addressed more specifically to those of you for whom binge eating has become a significant daily problem. Binge eating disorder is a serious behavioural disorder. It should never be taken lightly: Not only can it have consequences for physical health, but it also causes profound mental distress.

Although help from a specialist is often necessary, this chapter will suggest several potential solutions to guide you on your journey and help you better understand the causes of your pain. It may also be helpful to those around you, who will have a better idea of what you're going through.

First, let's specify the criteria for diagnosing binge eating disorder, as laid out in the *Diagnostic and Statistical Manual of Mental Disorders* (5th edition), also known as the DSM-5.

A. Recurrent episodes of binge eating. An episode of binge eating is characterized by both of the following:

   I. Eating, in a discrete period of time (e.g., within any 2-hour period), an amount of food that is definitely larger than what most people would eat in a similar period of time under similar circumstances.

2. A sense of lack of control over eating during the episode (e.g., a feeling that one cannot stop eating or control what or how much one is eating).

B. The binge-eating episodes are associated with three (or more) of the following:

1. Eating much more rapidly than normal.
2. Eating until feeling uncomfortably full.
3. Eating large amounts of food when not feeling physically hungry.
4. Eating alone because of feeling embarrassed by how much one is eating.
5. Feeling disgusted with oneself, depressed, or very guilty afterward.

C. Marked distress regarding binge eating is present.

D. The binge eating occurs, on average, at least once a week for 3 months.

E. The binge eating is not associated with the recurrent use of inappropriate compensatory behavior as in bulimia nervosa and does not occur exclusively during the course of bulimia nervosa or anorexia nervosa.

Specify if:
  In partial remission: After full criteria for binge-eating disorder were previously met, binge eating occurs at an average frequency of less than one episode per week for a sustained period of time.

In full remission: After full criteria for binge-eating disorder were previously met, none of the criteria have been met for a sustained period of time.

Specify current severity:
The minimum level of severity is based on the frequency of episodes of binge eating (see below). The level of severity may be increased to reflect other symptoms and the degree of functional disability.

Mild: 1–3 binge-eating episodes per week.
Moderate: 4–7 binge-eating episodes per week.
Severe: 8–13 binge-eating episodes per week.
Extreme: 14 or more binge-eating episodes per week.[1]
(See appendix 1.)

When food becomes a constant obsession

Eating quickly, consuming a larger-than-normal amount, and feeling very guilty afterward are all signs of a binge eating episode.

Generally, in people with an eating disorder, two kinds of binge eating episodes[2] can be observed:

- **Subjective:** the person eats normally but has the sense of losing control and feels very guilty about his or her behaviour. This type of binge eating episode usually involves fewer than 1,000 calories on average—for example, having two or three cookies, or a meal consisting of normal serving sizes.

- **Objective:** the person eats large amounts with a sense of loss of control and guilt. This type of episode involves more than 1,000 calories on average—for example, consuming a big bag of chips and half a jar of chocolate spread eaten with a spoon, or two rows of cookies and a quart of ice cream.

In people with binge eating disorder, both kinds of binge eating episodes may be present. However, objective episodes have to occur at the frequency indicated on page 155 for a diagnosis to be clearly established.

During a binge eating episode, some binge eaters, if alone, will swallow any food within reach—fresh, canned, or frozen—and in a short span of time. In contrast to people with bulimia, compulsive eaters do not engage in purging behaviours like vomiting, overuse of laxatives or diuretics, fasting, or extreme physical activity. As a result, many of them carry excess weight, often more than 50 pounds.

True or false?

Obese people all have binge eating disorder.

False

Contrary to widespread belief, binge eating affects 5 to 10 percent of obese people, and roughly a third of obese individuals report having binge eating attacks from time to time.[3, 4] This means that two-thirds of obese people do not necessarily experience a sense of loss of control even if they eat more.

"I never would have thought that one day I would be a compulsive overeater. However, food has always held an important place in my life. I loved sugar, which was also a reward (dessert, ice cream on weekends and for family parties, etc.). I was very athletic, so I didn't have any weight problems. It was around age 35 that food became a problem, following a period of exhaustion and anxiety.

I remember my first binge eating episode vividly. One afternoon when I felt especially depressed, with no self-esteem, I momentarily felt very good while eating a lot of sweet foods. From then on I binged every day, which resulted in a significant weight gain. Unfortunately, this lasted several years. In particular, I felt terribly guilty to be constantly giving in to eating fits that obsessed me from morning to night!

During this time I tried all kinds of drastic diets (protein, fasts, etc.), none of which worked because I kept having relapses. After losing some weight I'd start eating again and then some. The result: another drop in my self-esteem and a return to bingeing . . .

After many years of obsessing, of suffering, I heard about a support group for eating disorders from a co-worker. For the first time in my life, I understood that for me sugar was an addiction just like drugs or alcohol. The first stage in my new lifestyle was the most difficult: accepting that I was powerless around food and that I had lost control over my life.

I remember very well the worst day of my life. It was when I left work in the middle of the day, completely *dejected, to meet Isabelle at her clinic. I had hit rock bottom and I wanted everything to stop.*

Today, with her advice, my support group, a lot of reading, and sessions with a psychologist, I'm gradually learning to get back on my feet; one day at a time . . ."

—Claude

Understanding the causes of the disease

When we're consumed day after day by a problem that takes over most of our thoughts, it's absolutely normal to ask ourselves why this is happening to us and to try to understand where the problem comes from.

What are the factors that have contributed to the development of this unhealthy relationship with food?

By probing into a patient's weight and emotional history since childhood, we often manage to identify the familial patterns that have led to a food dependency. For instance: a mother obsessed by her own weight who constantly makes remarks about her daughter's curves; a mother who forces her child to clean his or her plate; a mother-daughter co-dependency; an incestuous father; a teenage rape victim; a battered woman. Patients without a complicated past are a rarity.

Treatment requires considering the causes underlying the illness. You can't treat the disease without knowing where it comes from. Previous dependency on alcohol, narcotics, or hard drugs is often reported; transfer from one dependency to another is common. A weight-loss diet can never erase deep-seated wounds and must often be combined with psychological therapy.

Are genetics at fault?

Genetics might also be a factor in binge eating disorder.[5, 6] The role of genetics in each eating disorder, as a percentage, is as follows:[7]

The role of genetics in eating disorders

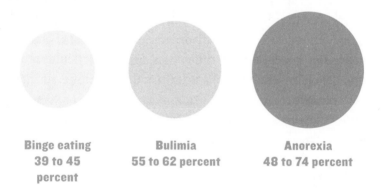

Binge eating	Bulimia	Anorexia
39 to 45 percent	55 to 62 percent	48 to 74 percent

The chart highlights recent data indicating that binge eating has a strong genetic basis. Our eating behaviours also depend on our genes.

After seeing these statistics, one of our female clients worried, "Does that mean I'll have my eating disorder all my life?"

It's important to clarify that just because genetics are a factor in eating disorders, it does not mean that developing an eating disorder is inevitable and that it's impossible to get over it once you have it. It simply means you have a higher-than-average chance of developing the disorder if other factors are present, and that in order to remain in remission once you're well, you'll have to take better care of yourself than the average person does.

What other problems coincide with binge eating?

Like most eating disorders, it's not unusual for binge eating to occur with other problems. Sexual abuse[8], low self-esteem, mood disorders, anxiety disorders, perfectionism, alcohol dependency, relationship difficulties, and in particular attention deficit hyperactivity disorder[9] are all problems associated with binge eating. It's important to assess ADHD and symptoms of depression systematically, as they very often accompany binge eating disorder.

Do people with binge eating disorder have personality traits in common?

When you have binge eating disorder, it's not uncommon to view the world as dangerous, to believe that people are against you or judge you harshly. This is understandable when, for example, you have a history of abuse and you view the world through depressive thoughts. There is a link between border-line personality disorder and binge eating disorder in 6 to 30 percent of binge eating disorder cases.[10] Borderline personality disorder traits include a fear of abandonment, instability in relationships, a feeling of not knowing who you are, a sense of emptiness, impulsivity, self-destructive behaviours, etc. These traits increase vulnerability to developing and maintaining an eating disorder.

We often see situations in which people give a great deal to others and then think that others are treating them badly by not giving as much back, even though they never dare to ask directly for what they need. These people often manage strong emotions in ways that punish themselves. For example, a client who is angry at her doctor because he made a remark about her weight but doesn't say anything to him might take her anger out on herself by going on a binge. When younger, she didn't learn how to assert herself and express her negative feelings.

What kinds of families do people with binge eating disorder have?

Sometimes we observe similarities in the families of people with an eating disorder. However, it's important not to over-generalize, because in many cases the family dynamics were completely normal. For example, there are cases of eating disorders in children even when their parents were loving and warm-hearted and respected limits.

For binge eating disorder, many studies report paren-tal neglect, the perception of parental rejection, critical comments about the child's weight, early exposure to dieting, and childhood obesity.[11] In other words, a lot of focus on weight and little parental acceptance of the child as they are.

Possible treatments

Treatment for binge eating disorder, as with other eating disorders, is influenced by the origins of the disease, which consist of a complex interaction of hereditary, psychological, and environmental factors that must be taken into account. The primary objective is to prevent binge eating attacks. When a person is significantly overweight or has physical problems related to excess weight, a gradual weight-loss diet is proposed first, in order to achieve healthy and long-lasting weight loss. Treatment should also target motivation; education about a healthier diet and lifestyle; modification of dysfunctional thoughts and habits; increased knowledge of, and ability to manage, conflicts and negative emotions; care for physical (diabetes, cholesterol, high blood pressure, for example) and psychological comorbidities; and prevention of relapses. Ideally, treatment should emphasize healthy food habits rather than a weight-loss diet. The sooner binge eating disorder is detected, the faster the recovery.

Several treatment options for binge eating disorder[12] exist. What you choose will depend on what services you can access in your area, your financial resources, and how much time you can devote to treatment. There's no single solution, so don't look for one. Instead, try to identify the combination of treatments that meets your needs. In the preceding chapters, we've described a number of techniques. These include:

Cognitive behavioural therapy

According to the definition of the Institut universitaire en santé mentale de Montréal,[13] cognitive behavioural therapy (or cognitive-behaviour therapy) is a psychotherapy focused on modifying problematic thoughts and behaviours. This therapy has four main objectives:

1. Create a solid therapeutic relationship so as to educate patients about compulsive eating and its causes.

2. Arrive at a normal diet by integrating behavioural strategies, such as using a food diary.

3. Restructure inaccurate thoughts about food, body image, and interpersonal relations, and thus succeed in better managing emotions.

4. Maintain progress and prevent relapses in the long term by identifying techniques to use to manage future risk factors.

This therapy can be described as usually active, directive, structured, and relatively short in duration (about 20 sessions). It's currently the therapy of choice for binge eating disorder. The remission rates over 12 months are very promising.[14]

In cognitive-behaviour therapy you can expect to begin the session with an analysis of your food diary. Next, you and your psychologist will discuss subjects related to your eating disorder such as compensatory behaviours, for example. You'll be weighed and you'll explore your feelings around your weight, and then you and your therapist will agree on an objective for the coming week, with remission as a goal.

Behavioural weight-loss therapy

Behavioural weight-loss therapy is based on diet and lifestyle changes for significant loss of weight. This therapy has been borrowed from the treatment for obesity, but a number of studies have shown it to be just as effective in treating binge eating disorder, especially if the weight loss continues after attacks have been reduced or stabilized.

For those rare patients without psychopathologies (depression, anxiety, etc.) related to the disorder, results are noticeable, and even comparable to more complex therapies. This is why the therapy is of great interest for people with binge eating disorder, who are significantly dissatisfied with their bodies. Even though weight is not directly related to the severity of binge eating, it's very much involved in many medical problems, as well as mood and self-esteem issues.

The caloric restriction traditionally imposed in this therapy should be moderate; a normal or slightly lower calorie diet seems to be the best strategy for avoiding binge eating. Obviously, massive and rapid weight loss should be discouraged, given the increased risk of regaining weight. In this therapy, patients are not blamed if dietary recommendations aren't followed; instead, there's an emphasis on a collaborative approach to planning food intake. Excluding certain foods is *not* recommended. It's more useful to encourage patients to moderate the amount of food consumed according to their individual needs.

Dialectic behavioural therapy

This psychotherapy, initially designed for borderline personality disorder, has shown proven effectiveness for binge eating disorder. It focuses more on controlling emotions and managing distress than does cognitive behavioural therapy, and is especially appropriate when impulsivity is a part of the binge eating. It is as effective as cognitive behavioural therapy in reducing binge eating attacks and concerns about food and weight, but to date it hasn't shown clear results for weight loss, depression, or anxiety.

Psycho-educational intervention

The purpose of psycho-educational treatment for binge eating disorder is to provide information on the disease, so as to promote a deeper understanding of the disorder and equip patients with practical tools for managing it. Basic subjects—such as factors that predispose people to binge eating attacks and trigger and maintain them, the negative effects of drastic diets, and the most effective weight regulation methods—are discussed. Interventions focus simply on explaining symptoms—without, however, adopting strategies to influence the risky behaviours psychologically (in contrast to psychotherapies).

Psycho-educational interventions have shown preliminary effectiveness in reducing attacks and impulsive dietary behaviours, but the effects on body image, anxiety, symptoms of depression, and weight loss are still open to question. After considering this preliminary data, researchers have concluded that psycho-educational interventions are a basic therapy that may be useful when combined with more complete treatments. Future studies that include control groups will be needed, however.

Mindfulness-based methods

Meditation, distress tolerance techniques, mindful eating, and acceptance of emotions are techniques that reduce binge eating episodes. However, their effects on weight loss are still being debated. Mindfulness also consists of getting in touch with every behaviour and every emotion in the moment, accepting them without judgment. This could enable individuals to better identify and manage strong emotions and to learn to eat intuitively, while listening more attentively to their bodies.

Interpersonal therapy

This psychological treatment focuses on those interpersonal relations that may play a role in the predisposition to, and maintenance of, eating disorders. The goal of the therapy is to improve social interactions and the ability to manage conflicts. Although it does not concentrate directly on dietary symptoms, the therapy can be useful, since it targets the problems that can trigger attacks in some people with binge eating disorder. The theory is that it could be especially useful in individuals whose negative moods are a major binge eating trigger.

Drug therapy

While less effective than psychotherapy, medication can nonetheless help treat symptoms associated with binge eating disorder. Antidepressants are the most studied medications for treating binge eating disorder. Their effectiveness has been tested notably on the impulse to overeat. Those most often used to date act on serotonin and are part of the family of SSRIs—for example, Prozac (fluoxetine).[15]

Some appetite-suppressant drugs like topiramate (initially created as an anticonvulsant) have also been studied as drug therapy for their effects on binge eating symptoms. Some of them have shown a positive effect in reducing binge eating attacks and have caused weight loss when binge eating disorder is associated with obesity.[16] On the other hand, a number of side effects have been reported (headache, drowsiness), and more long-term studies are needed.

A new avenue currently being studied by pharmaceutical companies is the use of a drug called Vyvanse (lisdexamfetamine dimesylate), originally formulated for ADHD. According to preliminary studies, this drug may help manage binge eating attacks by acting on impulsivity and attention.[17] Since ADHD is often associated with binge eating, this connection is easy to understand. The data are still in the embryonic stages.

Bariatric surgery

According to current recommendations, bariatric surgery is a treatment for severe obesity (BMI greater than or equal to 40 or BMI greater than or equal to 30 with comorbidity). It's not a treatment especially designed for obese people with binge eating disorder, but it may improve mood and thus act as a protective factor against vulnerability to binge eating attacks. That makes it a useful option in cases of severe obesity related to binge eating disorder. However, while some studies show that people with binge eating disorder lose as much weight and maintain the results just as well as obese people without binge eating disorder, other studies, in contrast, have found that binge eating disorder is associated with a higher risk of post-operative complications, less weight loss, and a greater probability of regaining the lost weight. The choice therefore depends on the binge eater's personal situation. Combining bariatric surgery with long-term therapy, to increase the chances of successful treatment, is strongly recommended. Note that the weight loss still depends on whether attacks resume after surgery.

"*I had a difficult childhood: there's no pity for obese children. Other children and even adults don't appreciate the wounds left by jokes or innocent little remarks that are part of daily life for an obese child. I chose humour to differentiate myself and stand out from the crowd. There were other options: violence, self-pity, or denial. But the latter is harder to maintain, since the truth jumps out at you every time you look in a mirror. Among other irritants were sports; physical education; the seat-belt extension on planes; clothes that don't fit—except ones that are the same colour as your sofa cushions; change that falls on the ground that you pretend not to see; and of course the booth at the restaurant where the table saws you in two and you say no, everything's okay.*

The overeater cannot hide or pretend, contrary to other dependencies. It's obvious at first sight, even if you order a Diet Coke with your poutine . . .

When the option of bariatric surgery was offered to me, I hesitated, telling myself I should be able to manage my dependency by myself and not with an operation. Then I realized that this was a gift life was offering me and not a failure on my part.

Since the operation, nine months ago already, much has changed. I've lost 90 pounds, I've gone from five daily injections of insulin to zero, I've changed my wardrobe three times, I'm richer now that I can pick up the quarters and dollars that have fallen on the ground, and I always choose the booth at a restaurant . . . The surgery has not solved everything, but yes, my life is better; every day I am a little more aware of my new status, of the remarks of those around me, of the choice of the size of my trousers, and of course of my relationship with mirrors, which has improved. I believe in personal change, I believe in life, and I especially believe you have to remain open to its gifts."

—Réal

A number of our patients with binge eating disorder are considering, or have had, bariatric surgery. It is an option to consider in cases of morbid obesity, since the condition threatens the life of the affected person in the short term. Morbid obesity is an urgent, dangerous situation, and classic weight loss may take too much time. We've met clients who have had a bariatric procedure twice, the first time without external support. Despite the modification of the stomach's capacity, if you haven't learned to manage your emotions other than by compulsive eating, the nightmare will begin again. The stomach will grow larger, and physical pain and vomiting may occur during each attack—not to mention possible complications during each operation for someone in precarious health. In short, bariatric surgery is an extreme treatment, to be turned to when excess weight results in urgent health problems. It isn't magical, and if the underlying problem hasn't been resolved through therapy, it will very likely recur. Some hospitals require a candidate for surgery to first undergo at least two years of psychotherapy to work on the problem underlying the obesity.

In summary

An increasing number of options are now available for treating patients with binge eating disorder. Cognitive behavioural therapy and interpersonal therapy reduce binge eating behaviours in the short and long term and are considered the treatments of choice for binge eating. Other useful treatments include behavioural-weight loss therapy; methods that rely on mindfulness; and dialectic behavioural therapy. These treatments are effective in reducing binge eating attacks, with varying results for associated weight loss. Antidepressants may also be moderately useful in treating binge eating disorder, including treating the depressive symptoms associated with it, but their long-term effects have not been studied. Finally, for people with binge eating disorder and severe obesity with complications associated with obesity who have not responded adequately to psychotherapy or drug therapy, bariatric surgery may be considered. In short, important progress has recently been made in developing treatments for binge eating disorder, but more research is needed.

"Binge eating began to interfere with my life in my early thirties after my pregnancy with twins, a period during which I placed great importance on the quality of my food choices. I approached the next 14 months, while I breastfed my boys, with the same determination, wanting to give them the best of myself. Even though I didn't feel any pressure to do so and didn't feel like I was sacrificing myself, I had nonetheless taken a certain degree of control over my life and established a number of food prohibitions that, gradually, became entrenched. In the months after I stopped breastfeeding, this pressure eased. I found myself in front of the television every evening with my bag of chips and my chocolates as a kind of 'reward' or escape from this new life as a mother—which I loved and had under control, but which brought with it its own challenges and new realities. Since I had never paid attention to what I ate and how much, I found myself with a body and a feeling of unhappiness I had never before known. I'd lost my bearings. After a few months of this downward spiral, I decided to visit the CHANGE clinic, which specializes in eating disorders.

The individual therapy I had for several months was a great help in identifying destructive behaviours, but I think the group therapy meetings also provided huge support. Talking to women who had struggles similar to mine regarding self-esteem, poor body image, and limited self-confidence helped me reduce the pressure or discomfort I felt in coping with binge eating disorder all by myself.

I wanted to learn how to come to terms with this disorder—which will always be lurking inside me—so as not to be at its beck and call. To rediscover the happiness and well-being of life and eat in a healthy way. To provide an example that is inspiring and free of dependency to my children, so they can enjoy eating healthily without pressure or prohibitions to manage.

Some tools that help me:

- *Plan a day's meals so I don't have to make decisions when mealtimes inevitably roll around and then make bad choices that can lead to regrets or judgments.*

- *Eat at regular intervals and always have healthy snacks handy, which eliminates the possibility of finding myself starving at mealtimes and eating a larger amount of food.*

- *Keep active with running and yoga, without overdoing it but just to have it as part of my life, since I know and feel this does me a lot of good. If I put this on hold sometimes, I feel an enormous need to go back to it—for my physical well-being, of course, but especially for my psychological well-being.*

- *I now know which situations make me more vulnerable to this disease. When I have sporadic attacks, I refer to the techniques I learned in therapy, and that quickly gets me back on the right track."*

—*Claudianne*

Support from family and friends

An eating disorder involves the entire family. Spouse, children, parents, and friends need to support loved ones with the disorder so that they can work toward a cure. Sufferers, for their part, must remember that food does not have their best interests at heart but YOU love them and do! Recommendations for friends and family to help loved ones stay in remission follow.

How to best support someone with binge eating disorder

I. **Avoid comments on weight and body image.**
   Even when someone with a binge eating disorder asks you to, it's never actually helpful to comment on weight or body image, whether negatively or positively. In addition, avoid commenting on your own weight or your own body image. Remember—the issue isn't weight, since even if the person lost weight, binge eating disorder would not disappear. Weight is just the tip of the iceberg.

Say, instead: "How are you? Tell me how you're doing at the moment."

2. **Avoid intervening during binge eating attacks or compensatory behaviours.**

   Taking, for example, a bag of chips away from someone you love will not make the binge eating episodes stop. On the contrary—it will encourage binge eating alone, in secret. The same is true for vomiting or other compensatory behaviours; knocking on the washroom door will only push the person away from you.

   Say, instead: "I have the feeling things are hard for you right now. Want to talk to me about it? If not, would going out to do something with me help you feel better? I'm here for you."

3. **Take time to learn about the disease—become an expert.**

   It can be easy to rush to judgment when we eat normally and the person we love seems to take so long to recover from an eating disorder. It seems so simple to you; so how come the person you care about can't eat normally? Yet binge eating disorder is one of the hardest-to-treat mental health problems.

   Take the time to do some reading, to attend support groups for families or spouses. It will help you better understand the tough battle your loved one is fighting.

4. **Don't bear the burden alone.**

   If the person you love confides in you about an eating disorder, don't bear the weight of this secret by yourself. The disease can have considerable consequences for physical health, sometimes even putting the lives of sufferers in danger. Minimizing symptoms is part of the disease, so your loved one may not be aware of the seriousness of the situation.

   Encourage the person to tell their doctor about it, to talk to others around them, and to find a psychologist. Contact Crisis Services Canada at any time at 1-833-456-4566 if the person mentions suicidal thoughts.

5. **Don't play saviour.**

   For various reasons, spouses sometimes try on their own to save people who have binge eating disorder. Doing so can make you feel good about yourself at the beginning; but even if you understand your partner's problem perfectly, it won't translate into permanent changes because you're not a therapist. Worse still, lies and negative emotions can poison your relationship as a couple.

   Encourage your partner to take care of himself or herself, but foremost to go and get help. Emphasize small successes and strengthen your bond by sharing feelings, including vulnerabilities.

Remember

✓ If you have binge eating disorder, you are not alone; there are more and more resources to help you get better.

✓ Educating those close to you about your eating disorder is important if you want them to provide you with the support you need.

✓ Take the time to have the problems that go along with binge eating disorder (ADHD, depression, sexual abuse, personality traits, etc.) assessed and treated.

CONCLUSION

Taking action to change a long-standing problem sometimes seems like trying to change the path of the sun. But sensitizing ourselves to the consequences of binge eating on the body and taking the time to identify those that we're experiencing can really increase our determination to change.

To succeed in curbing your binge eating, you need to weigh what it's costing you against what it gives back to you, in the short and long term. For example, planning and carrying around snacks may be tiresome, but that's less bothersome than having excess weight or high blood pressure limit your daily activities. Here's a table to help you think through your motivations:

BENEFITS AND COSTS OF CHANGING			
Advantages of changing how I deal with my eating problem		Downsides of changing how I deal with my eating problem	
In the short term:	In the long term:	In the short term:	In the long term:

From now on, ask yourself:

What challenges will I face by changing, and what solutions can I come up with?

CHALLENGES	SOLUTIONS

You may be asking yourself where to start . . . This book contains a lot of information, and you will no doubt have to read it again to really put into practice our various pieces of advice. To help you begin your journey, here is a summary of our best strategies:

Our top 10 strategies

1. **Apply the 3–3–3 rule.**
   This means eating three balanced meals and three snacks containing carbohydrate and protein every day, and never going more than about three hours without eating.

2. **Keep a food diary that takes your emotions into account.**
   It's important to understand what makes you lose control. Is it loneliness, boredom, anxiety? Once you've figured out which emotions cause attacks, you can deal with them more effectively by replacing them with an activity that's good for you. You'll find a template in appendix 4 to help you.

3. **Draw up a list of trigger foods.**
   It may be chocolate, caramel sauce, ice cream, etc. First of all, get rid of any foods that cause you to lose control on a weekly basis. Once the attacks have decreased, allow some trigger foods back on the menu, but eat them in safe environments. For example, have a piece of cheesecake when you're out with friends; you won't be tempted later to eat the rest of it because you won't have access to

it. Reintroduce trigger foods into your house gradually, over several months.

4. **Learn to assert yourself.**
People who binge eat often have trouble asserting themselves. By working on being able to say what you think and feel, you learn to manage your attacks better.

5. **Avoid diets.**
Severe diets cause obesity by sabotaging your natural weight. Aim for a normal diet and take care of *all* aspects of your life.

6. **Exercise.**
Being active is definitely part of the solution, and this is true regardless of your physical condition. By releasing endorphins, physical activity boosts mood, resulting in a better relationship with food and your body.

7. **Get support.**
Nutritionists, mentors, psychologists, psycho-educators, social workers, and physicians are some of the people who can provide the support you need to start your journey. For best results, support from your spouse and your family are also needed.

8. **Eat mindfully.**
By taking the time to sit down and savour every mouthful, you enjoy the moment. You owe it to yourself to avoid eating from the corner of the kitchen counter, in a

rush—because swallowing without savouring is not eating mindfully. During a binge eating episode, we eat two and a half times faster than average. Notice the difference when you're neither restricting yourself nor blocking out a negative emotion with food.

9. **Set yourself a realistic objective.**
Most clients come to the clinic wanting to lose weight. (Many even hope to return to the size they were at 20!) When you no longer eat emotionally and eliminate binge eating, weight loss is likely, even without restricting calories. However, the first goal should not be to lose weight but to improve your relationship with food and, foremost, with yourself. Avoid setting a weight-loss objective at the start of treatment.

10. **Love yourself more.**
Self-esteem is greatly affected by eating disorders. When you learn to have confidence in yourself, to have compassion for yourself rather than to criticize yourself constantly, to pay attention to your physical and psychological qualities, you can't help but manage your food intake better.

Recovering from an eating disorder, or even resisting the binge eating that is a response to emotional needs, is a major struggle. You will need time and resources. You don't have to do it on our own. Talk about it with those close to you, and don't let shame or guilt isolate you. If you feel the need, join a support group and find a specialized professional who will know how to assist you in this undertaking.

All the best on your journey,
Isabelle and Catherine

APPENDIX

1

EATING BEHAVIOUR DISORDERS

Eating behaviour disorders are a large group of conditions characterized by an unhealthy relationship with food, weight, or body image, with serious consequences for physical health and psychosocial activities. The group includes several highly complex disorders and behaviours. The reasons eating behaviour disorders develop are not entirely clear. Those suffering from them, however, all share low self-esteem, anxiety, and feelings of loneliness.

The best-known eating disorders are anorexia nervosa and bulimia. The main ones are described in the DSM-5, the fifth edition of the *Diagnostic and Statistical Manual of Mental Disorders*, published and updated periodically by the American Psychiatric Association.

Anorexia (anorexia nervosa)

People with anorexia have an intense fear of gaining weight and have a distorted body image. They believe they're overweight even when their weight is too low. They're usually on weight-loss diets and get a lot of physical exercise; they may count calories obsessively and only allow themselves tiny servings of certain, very specific foods. When presented with the facts, they will often deny they have a problem. Because they're good at hiding their disorder, it can become serious before anyone notices anything. Untreated, anorexia can lead to threatening complications such as malnutrition and various organ failures. However, most people who are treated will regain their lost weight and recover from the physical problems that have developed.

Diagnostic criteria for anorexia

- Restriction of energy intake relative to requirements, leading to a significantly low body weight for age, sex, developmental trajectory, and physical health.

- Intense fear of gaining weight or becoming fat, or persistent behaviour that interferes with weight gain, even though weight is significantly low.

- Disturbance in the way in which body weight or shape is experienced, undue influence of body weight or shape on self-evaluation, or persistent lack of recognition of the seriousness of the current low body weight.

Types of anorexia

1. **Restricting type:** During the last three months, the individual has not engaged in recurrent episodes of binge eating or purging behaviour (self-induced vomiting or the misuse of laxatives, diuretics, or enemas).

This subtype presents with weight loss accomplished primarily through dieting, fasting, or excessive physical exercise.

2. Binge eating/purging type (with bulimia or compensatory behaviours): During the last three months, the individual has engaged in recurrent episodes of binge eating or purging behaviour (self-induced vomiting or the misuse of laxatives, diuretics, or enemas).

Severity of the disease

The severity for adults is based on body mass index (BMI), and for children and adolescents on BMI percentile. The ranges that follow are derived from World Health Organization categories for thinness in adults.

Mild: BMI > 17 kg/m^2

Moderate: BMI 16–16.99 kg/m^2

Severe: BMI 15–15.99 kg/m^2

Extreme: BMI < 15 kg/m^2

Bulimia (bulimia nervosa)

People with bulimia have episodes during which they eat very large amounts of food (called binge eating). The main characteristic of this disorder is that following these episodes, bulimic individuals purge (by vomiting or laxative use), fast, or exercise rigorously to compensate for overeating. Contrary to people with anorexia, people with bulimia often have a relatively normal weight, but they still have the same intense fear of gaining weight and have a distorted body image. They believe they're "fat" and desperately want to lose weight. Often feeling ashamed and disgusted with themselves, they become very good at hiding their bulimic behaviours. In the long term, left untreated, bulimia can cause serious health problems such as cardiac arrhythmias, esophageal bleeding due to too much gastric acid, dental problems, and kidney problems.

Diagnostic criteria for bulimia

- Recurrent episodes of binge eating, characterized by both of the following:

    1. Eating, in a discrete period of time (for example, within any two-hour period), an amount of food that is definitely larger than what most individuals would eat in a similar period under similar circumstances.

2. A sense of lack of control over eating during the episode (a feeling that one cannot stop eating or control what or how much one is eating).

• Recurrent inappropriate compensatory behaviours in order to prevent weight gain, such as self-induced vomiting; misuse of laxatives, diuretics, or other medications; fasting; or excessive exercise.

• The binge eating and inappropriate compensatory behaviours both occur, on average, at least once a week for three months.

• Self-evaluation is unduly influenced by body shape and weight.

Severity of the disease

Severity is based on the frequency of inappropriate compensatory behaviours.

Mild: An average of 1–3 episodes of inappropriate compensatory behaviours per week.

Moderate: An average of 4–7 episodes of inappropriate compensatory behaviours per week.

Severe: An average of 8–13 episodes of inappropriate compensatory behaviours per week.

Extreme: An average of 14 or more episodes of inappropriate compensatory behaviours per week.

Other eating disorders

Some cases do not entirely correspond to the diagnostic criteria for anorexia or bulimia. Nonetheless, these are also eating behaviour disorders.

- **Atypical anorexia nervosa:** All the criteria for anorexia nervosa are met, except that despite significant weight loss, the individual's weight is within or above the normal range.

- **Bulimia nervosa** (of low frequency and/or limited duration): All the criteria for bulimia nervosa are met, except that the binge eating and inappropriate compensatory behaviours occur, on average, less than once a week and/or for less than three months.

- **Binge eating disorder** (of low frequency and/or limited duration): All the criteria for binge eating disorder are met, except that the binge eating occurs, on average, less than once a week and/or for less than three months.

- **Purging disorder:** Recurrent purging behaviour to influence weight or shape (for example, self-induced vomiting; misuse of laxatives, diuretics, or other medications) in the absence of binge eating.

- **Night-eating syndrome:** Recurrent episodes of night eating, as manifested by eating after awakening from sleep or by excessive food consumption after the evening meal. The night eating is not caused by changes in the sleep-wake cycle or by social norms, or by another disorder or another mental disorder (including substance abuse), and is not attributable to another medical disorder or to a side effect of medication.

Binge eating and possible eating disorders

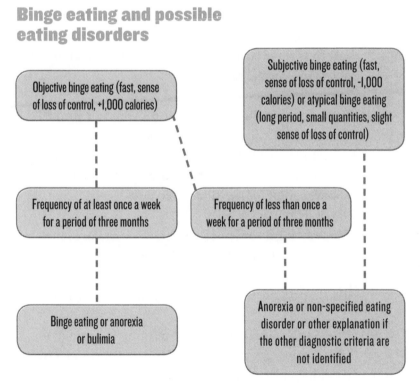

Objective binge eating (fast, sense of loss of control, +1,000 calories)

Subjective binge eating (fast, sense of loss of control, -1,000 calories) or atypical binge eating (long period, small quantities, slight sense of loss of control)

Frequency of at least once a week for a period of three months

Frequency of less than once a week for a period of three months

Binge eating or anorexia or bulimia

Anorexia or non-specified eating disorder or other explanation if the other diagnostic criteria are not identified

Have you noticed that binge eating can occur in most eating disorders?

The SCOFF questionnaire

Developed in 1999,[3] this very simple questionnaire takes only a few seconds to complete and is used to quickly establish potential anorexia or bulimia. If you answer yes to at least two questions, you might have an eating disorder, and seeing a specialist is suggested.

	YES	NO
1. Do you make yourself **S**ick because you feel uncomfortably full?	☐	☐
2. Do you worry that you have lost **C**ontrol over how much you eat?	☐	☐
3. Have you recently lost [**O**ver 15 pounds] in a three-month period?	☐	☐
4. Do you believe yourself to be **F**at when others say you are too thin?	☐	☐
5. Would you say that **F**ood dominates your life?	☐	☐

LIST OF EMOTIONS

Abandoned	Embarrassed	Misunderstood
Admiring	Energetic	Offended
Aggressive	Envious	Pitiful
Alone	Excited	Powerless
Ambivalent	Fearful	Proud
Amused	Fulfilled	Rejected
Angry	Guilty	Relieved
Anxious	Happy	Resentful
Apprehensive	Humiliated	Rushed
Astonished	Hurt	Sad
Betrayed	In love	Stressed
Bored	Indecisive	Surprised
Calm	Indifferent	Tired
Confident	Insecure	Unsatisfied
Confused	Intimidated	Useless
Curious	Irritable	Vulnerable
Despairing	Jealous	Wary
Disappointed	Loved	Weary
Disgusted	Loving	Worn down

APPENDIX

LIST OF RESOURCES

National services and resources

Canadian Public Health Association

This national non-profit organization provides an array of online health resources and advocates for improved healthcare policies to the federal government.

https://www.cpha.ca/

Health Canada

Health Canada is a federal institution with extensive online resources on topics such as nutrition, healthy lifestyles, food safety, and ongoing public health concerns.

https://www.canada.ca/en/health-canada.html

Kids Help Phone

Kids Help Phone provides Canadian youth with health information and
support 24 hours a day, 7 days a week.

https://kidshelpphone.ca/

National Eating Disorder Information Centre (NEDIC)

NEDIC focuses on eating disorder awareness and prevention, providing
such services as workshops, awareness campaigns, and a toll-free helpline. They also have a directory of over 600 service providers across the
country, to help Canadians find local resources. The helpline hours are
Monday to Thursday 9 a.m. to 9 p.m. EST and Friday 9 a.m. to 5 p.m. EST.

1-866-NEDIC-20 (1-866-633-4220)

416-340-4156 in Toronto/GTA

http://www.nedic.ca/

Services and resources by province

Alberta

Eating Disorder Support Network of Alberta

EDSNA provides online resources on eating disorders, hosts an annual
Eating Disorders Awareness Week, and offers professionally facilitated
support groups in Edmonton, Calgary, and online.

http://edsna.ca/about-us/#about

British Columbia

Kelty Eating Disorders

Kelty Eating Disorders is British Columbia's hub of eating disorder-related resources and services, including thorough explanations of various disorders, how they can be treated, and where to find help. Resources are offered in multiple languages.

https://keltyeatingdisorders.ca/

Manitoba

Eating Disorders Manitoba

Eating Disorders Manitoba provides facts on eating disorders, recommended reading, and treatment information for both teenagers and adults.

http://eatingdisordersmanitoba.ca/

New Brunswick

Maritime Psychology Clinic

Dedicated to mental health services in general, the Maritime Psychology Clinic offers eating disorder information such as debunked myths and tips for resisting unhealthy eating behaviour.

506-855-5515

info@maritimepsychologyclinic.ca

https://www.maritimepsychologyclinic.ca/resources-for-adults/eating-disorders

Newfoundland and Labrador

Eating Disorder Foundation of Newfoundland and Labrador

The EDFNL is a leadership advocacy group committed to providing an
effective and informative system of support services for those affected by
eating disorders in Newfoundland and Labrador.

http://edfnl.ca/

Nova Scotia

Eating Disorder Treatment Network, Nova Scotia

Led by the Nova Scotia Health Authority's Eating Disorders Clinic, the
Eating Disorder Treatment Network connects patients and health professionals from across the province.

https://www.cdha.nshealth.ca/eating-disorder-treatment-network-nova-scotia

Ontario

Bulimia Anorexia Nervosa Association

BANA is a non-profit organization providing eating disorder support in
southwest Ontario.

http://www.bana.ca/

Ontario Community Outreach Program for Eating Disorders

OCOPED is a partnership between the eating disorder programs at Toronto
General Hospital and the Hospital for Sick Children. Their "About Us"
page includes a downloadable list of treatment programs funded by the
Ontario Ministry of Health and Long-Term Care.

http://www.ocoped.ca/Home.aspx

Hopewell Eating Disorder Support Centre

Hopewell is a non-profit organization providing eating disorder support in eastern Ontario.

http://www.hopewell.ca/

Prince Edward Island

Community Mental Health Services

Community Mental Health offers information, treatment programs, referrals, and a helpline. Visit their webpage for the contact information of various locations across the province.

https://www.princeedwardisland.ca/en/information/health-pei/mental-health-services

Quebec

Anorexie et Boulimie Québec

ANEB is a non-profit organization offering various low-cost services to people with eating disorders, including closed and open group sessions, a 24-hour helpline, and a chat line.

1-800-630-0907 and 514-630-0907

http://anebquebec.com/

ANEB has a chat line especially for teenagers and young adults from 14 to 18, who can speak directly with an online counsellor. They can use this service to ask questions—whether for themselves, a friend, or a family member—and get support or references.

http://anebados.com/

Douglas Mental Health University Institute, Eating Disorder Clinic

This Montreal hospital offers out-patient and in-patient services to those
over 18 with anorexia nervosa or bulimia (no services for binge eating, to
date). The eating disorder program is recognized as the most advanced in
Quebec. A medical referral is required to make an appointment. Young
people under 18 have access to child psychiatry programs.

514-761-6131, extension 2895

douglas.qc.ca

Maison l'Éclaircie

Maison l'Éclaircie is a Quebec City community organization for balance
and well-being, assisting those with anorexia, bulimia, orthorexia, eating
compulsions, and binge eating disorder. Several kinds of sessions are
offered (individual, group, family support). The group approach involves
three blocks of workshops spread over 15 weeks.

1-866-900-1076

maisoneclaircie.qc.ca

Saskatchewan

BridgePoint Center for Eating Disorders

BridgePoint provides province-wide eating disorder services in partnership
with Saskatchewan Health.

http://www.bridgepointcenter.ca/

Services and resources by territory

Northwest Territories

Pulse Nutrition YK

Registered dietitian Kathleen Hernder operates this Yellowknife-based
service, offering help with eating disorders, nutritional information, and
other facets of healthy eating.

http://www.pulsenutritionyk.com/

Nunavut

Government of Nunavut: Mental Health

The government of Nunavut offers comprehensive mental health services,
the Kamatsiaqtut Helpline, and a directory of mental health service
providers across the territory.

https://www.gov.nu.ca/health/information/mental-health

Yukon

Kelty Eating Disorders: Yukon Mental Health Services

Part of the broader efforts of Kelty Eating Disorders, these resources include
individual therapy sessions and DBT (dialectical behavioural therapy)
skills modules.

https://keltyeatingdisorders.ca/yukon-eating-disorders-program/

APPENDIX

4

YOUR DIARY

Now it's your turn! Fill in your diary—it will become a valuable tool to help you regain control of your emotions and your diet.

TIME & CONTEXT	LEVEL OF HUNGER (0 TO 5)	WHAT I ATE AND/OR DRANK	LEVEL OF FULLNESS
Breakfast			
Snack			
Lunch			
Snack			
Dinner			
Snack			

EMOTION	AUTOMATIC THOUGHT	COGNITIVE DISTORTION	ALTERNATIVE THOUGHT

NOTES

Chapter 1

1. C. Fairburn, *Overcoming Binge Eating* (New York: Guilford Press), 2013, 11.

2. J. Polivy and C. Herman, "Etiology of binge eating: Psychological mechanisms," in C. G. Fairburn and G. T. Wilson (eds.), *Binge Eating: Nature, Assessment and Treatment* (New York: Guilford Press), 1993, 173–205.

3. C. P. Herman and D. Mack, "Restrained and unrestrained eating," *Journal of Personality* 43, 4 (1975): 647–660, http://dx.doi.org/10.1111/j.1467-6494.1975.tb00727.x.

4. C. Fairburn, *Cognitive Behavior Therapy and Eating Disorders* (New York: Guilford Press), 2008, 96–135.

5. Adapted from the healthyplace.com website.

Chapter 2

1. J. J. Wurtman and S. Suffes, *The Serotonin Solution to Achieve Permanent Weight Control* (New York: Random House), 1996.

Chapter 3

1. N. M. Avena, M. E. Bocarsly, and B. G. Hoebel, "Animal models of sugar and fat bingeing: Relationship to food addiction and increased body weight," *Methods of Molecular Biology* 829 (2012): 351–365.

2. M. L. Westwater, P. C. Fletcher, and H. Ziauddeen, "Sugar addiction: The state of science," *European Journal of Nutrition* 55 (Suppl. 2) (2016): 55–69. C. R. Markus, P. J. Rogers, F. Broun, and R. Schepers, "Eating dependence and weight gain: No human evidence for a 'sugar-addiction' model of overweight," *Appetite* 114 (2017), 64–72. doi: 10.1016/j.appet.2017.03.024. Epub 2017 Mar 19.

3. Z. Cooper, C. G. Fairburn, and D. B. Hawker, *Cognitive-Behavioral Treatment of Obesity* (New York: Guilford Press), 2003.

Chapter 4

1. D. D. Burns, *Être bien dans sa peau* (Les éditions Héritage), 1994, 46–56.

2. T. L. Ngô, L. Chaloult, and J. Goulet, *Guide de pratique pour le traitement du trouble dépressif majeur*, 2014, 11–16.

3. D. L. Safer, C. F. Telch, and E. Y. Chen, *Dialectical Behavior Therapy for Binge Eating and Bulimia* (New York: Guilford Press), 2009, 120–155.

4. M. M. Linehan, *Cognitive-Behavioral Treatment of Borderline Personality Disorder* (New York: Guilford Press), 1993, 199–219.

5. D. L. Safer, C. F. Telch, and E. Y. Chen, *Dialectical Behavior Therapy for Binge Eating and Bulimia* (New York: Guilford Press), 2009, 120–155.

6. Adapted from the book by Beaudry and Boisvert, *S'affirmer et communiquer* (Montréal, Éditions de l'Homme), 1979, 197–276.

Chapter 5

1. G. J. Wang et al., "Evidence of gender differences in the ability to inhibit brain activation elicited by food stimulation," *Proceedings of the National Academy of Sciences* 106, 4 (2009), 1249–1254; doi: 10.1073/pnas.0807423106. Epub 2009 Jan 21.

Chapter 6

1. D. L. Safer, C. F. Telch, and E. Y. Chen, *Dialectical Behavior Therapy for Binge Eating and Bulimia* (New York: Guilford Press), 2009, 120–155.

Chapter 7

1. T. F. Cash et al., "How has body image changed? A cross-sectional investigation of college women and men from 1983 to 2001," *Journal of Consulting and Clinical Psychology* 72, 6 (2004): 1081–1089.

2. A. C. Kelly and J. Carter, "Self-compassion training for binge eating disorder: A pilot randomized controlled trial," *Psychology and Psychotherapy: Theory, Research, and Practice* 88 (2015): 285–303.

3. C. Fairburn, *Cognitive Behavior Therapy and Eating Disorders* (New York: Guilford Press), 2008, 96–124.

4. D. F. Becker and C. M. Grilo, "Childhood maltreatment in women with binge-eating disorder: Associations with psychiatric comorbidity, psychological functioning, and eating pathology," *Eating and Weight Disorders: EWD* 16, 2 (2011): e113–e120.

5. T. Hildebrandt, K. Loeb, S. Troupe, and S. Delinsky, "Adjunctive mirror exposure for eating disorders: A randomized controlled pilot study," *Behavior Research Therapy* 50, 12 (2012): 797–804.

6. T. Field, M. Hernandez-Reif, and M. Diego, "Cortisol decreases and serotonin and dopamine increase following massage therapy," *International Journal of Neuroscience* 115 (2005): 1397–1413.

7. P. Gilbert and J. Miles, *Body Shame: Conceptualisation, Research and Treatment* (London: Taylor & Francis Group), 2014, 176.

8. L. Mahlo and M. Tiggermann, "Yoga and positive body image: A test of the embodiment model," *Body Image* 18 (September 2016): 135–142.

Chapter 8

1. American Psychiatric Association, *Diagnostic and Statistical Manual of Mental Disorders* (5th ed.), (Washington, DC: Author), 2013.

2. G. Fairburn and Z. Cooper, "The Eating Disorder Examination (12th edition)," in C. G. Fairburn and G. T. Wilson (eds.), *Binge Eating: Nature, Assessment and Treatment* (New York: Guilford Press), 1993, 317–360.

3. J. I. Hudson, E. Hiripi, H. G. Pope, and R. C. Kessler, "The prevalence and correlates of eating disorders in the National Comorbidity Survey Replication," *Biological Psychiatry* 61 (2007): 348–358.

4. C. M. Grilo, R. M. Masheb, and G. T. Wilson, "Efficacy of cognitive behavioral therapy and fluoxetine for the treatment of binge eating disorder: A randomized double-blind placebo-controlled comparison," *Biological Psychiatry* 57 (2005): 301–309.

5. C. M. Grilo and R. M. Masheb, "Childhood maltreatment and personality disorders in adult patients with binge eating disorder," *Acta Psychiatrica Scandinavica* 106 (2002): 183–188.

6. H. G. Pope Jr., et al., "Binge eating disorder: A stable syndrome," *American Journal of Psychiatry* 163, 12 (December 2006): 2181–2183.

7. Z. Yilmaz, A. Hardaway, and C. Bulik, "Genetics and epigenetics of eating disorders," *Advances in Genomics and Genetics* 5 (2015): 131–150.

8. L. Smolak and S. K. Murnen, "A meta-analytic examination of the relationship between child sexual abuse and eating disorders," *International Journal of Eating Disorders* 31 (2002): 136–150.

9. B. P. Nazar, et al., "Influence of attention-deficit/hyperactivity disorder on binge eating behaviors and psychiatric comorbidity profile of obese women," *Comprehensive Psychiatry* 55, 3 (2013): 572–578.

10. R. A. Sansone, M. W. Wiederman, and L. A. Sansone, "The prevalence of borderline personality disorder among individuals with obesity: A critical review of the literature," *Eating Behaviors* 1 (2000): 93–104.

11. C. M. Grilo and R. M. Masheb, "Childhood maltreatment and personality disorders in adult patients with binge eating disorder," *Acta Psychiatria Scandinavia* 106, (2002): 183–188.
J. I. Hudson, E. Hiripi, H. G. Pope, and R. C. Kessler, "The prevalence and correlates of eating disorders in the National Comorbidity Survey Replication," *Biological Psychiatry* 61 (2007): 348–358.

12. F. Amianto, L. Ottone, G. Abbate Daga and S. Fassino, "Binge-eating disorder diagnosis and treatment: A recap in front of DSM-5," *BMC Psychiatry* 15, 1 (2015): 70.

13. Institut universitaire en santé mentale de Montréal, *Thérapie d'approche cognitivo-comportementale* [online], http://www.iusmm.ca/hopital/usagers-/-famille/info-sur-la- sante-mentale/therapie-dapproche-cognitivo-comportementale.html.

14. C. M. Grilo, R. M. Masheb, T. Wilson, R. Gueorguieva and M. A. White, "Cognitive-behavioral therapy, behavorial weight loss and sequential treatment for obese patients with binge eating disorder: A randomized controlled trial," *Journal of Consulting and Clinical Psychology* 79, 5 (2011): 675–685.

15. F. Amianto et al., "Binge-eating disorder diagnosis and treatment: A recap in front of DSM-5," *BMC Psychiatry* 15, 1 (2015): 70.

16. S. L. McElroy et al., "Psychopharmacologic treatment of eating disorders: Emerging findings," *Current Psychiatry Reports* 17, 5 (2015): 1–7.

17. S. L. McElroy et al., "Lisdexamfetamine dimesylate effects on binge eating behaviour and obsessive-compulsive and impulsive features in adults with binge eating disorder," *European Eating Disorders Review* 24, 3 (2016): 223–231.

Appendix 1

1. Hudson, Hiripi, Pope, and Kessler, in K. Schaumberg et al., "The science behind the academy for eating disorders' nine truths about eating disorders." *European Eating Disorders Review* (2017), doi:10.1002/erv.2553.

2. K. Schaumberg et al., "The science behind the academy for eating disorders' nine truths about eating disorders." *European Eating Disorders Review* (2017), doi:10.1002/erv.2553.

3. J. F. Morgan, F. Reid, and J. H. Lacey, "*The SCOFF questionnaire: Assessment of a new screening tool for eating disorders,*" 319 (1999): 1467–1468.

ACKNOWLEDGEMENTS

Thank you to the entire team at Éditions de l'Homme, who never stopped believing in me and my many projects. A very special thanks to Judith Landry for supporting my ambitions, and to Pascale Mongeon, a thoughtful and meticulous editor, who helped us so intelligently throughout the writing of this book.

Thanks to my co-author, Catherine, who completed the book wonderfully with her scientifically rigorous research and her careful gathering together of all the recent data.

Thanks to Katherine Robert, who, during her internship in nutrition at Kilo Solution, spent several weeks listing studies on the classification of eating disorders and current therapies.

Thanks to Ginette, Natacha, Julie, Ève-Marie, Claude, and Réal, whose personal stories touched our hearts and those of our readers. Thanks to Véro, a long-time sufferer from eating disorders, for her reading and useful comments. Thanks to my friend Nancy, for having introduced me to this fascinating world more than 20 years ago.

Thanks to Sophie Grégoire Trudeau, a woman of influence whom I admire, for delivering such a meaningful and convincing message! Thank you, Sophie, for having shown confidence in us by contributing the foreword to this book.

And especially, thanks to the many people who have come to see me to overcome their disorders and whose experiences are at the heart of this book.

—Isabelle

Thanks to the entire team at Éditions de l'Homme for recognizing the relevance of this project and welcoming me so warmly.

Thanks to Isabelle Huot for having agreed to collaborate in writing this book, for helping me learn to popularize my scientific data, and for fostering a wonderful creative team process.

Thanks to D.L. and my colleague Marie-Hélène Bertrand for taking the time to edit the book by contributing your valuable comments.

Thanks to Jean-Marie, Annick, and Claudianne for sharing your experience with so much authenticity and selflessness.

Thanks to my beloved Patrick, William, and Victoria, and to my parents for having encouraged me to put this ambitious idea forward.

Thanks to my clients for putting as much of themselves as I do into our goal of a better tomorrow. This book is for you, inspired by you.

—Catherine

INDEX

comfort foods
    alternatives to, 69–70
    cravings for, 116–17
    as treats, 130
communication, 88
    of emotions, 129
    of needs, 146–47
Community Mental Health
    Services (PEI), 211
compassion (for self), 131–32, 186
compliments, 133
cortisol, 116, 138. *See also* stress
cosmetic surgery, 126
cravings
    for carbohydrates, 34–35
    for comfort foods, 116–17
    stress-related, 116–18
    for sugar, 35
Crisis Services Canada, 176
criticism
    expressing, 89–91
    receiving, 89

D

dairy products, 54
depression, 52, 160
    exercise and, 114
    and sleep, 101
Déry, Julie, 59–61
desserts, 28–29. *See also* sugar;
    treats

dialectic behavioural therapy, 82, 165,
    170–171
diaries
    for cognitive restructuring, 75–77
    of food intake, 103–6, 184, 216–17
    of personal thoughts, 36–39
diet. *See also* dieting; food
    adapting, 23–47
    balanced, 28–29
    carbohydrate in, 34–35, 117
    fibre in, 41
    gluten-free, 40
    protein in, 41
dieting
    avoiding, 25–26, 185
    as weight gain cause, 8, 9, 12
dopamine, 52, 70n, 138
Douglas Mental Health University
    Institute, Eating Disorder Clinic
    (QC), 212
drinks, 42, 54, 117. *See also* alcohol
drug therapies, 167–68, 171

E

eating. *See also* eating disorders
    compulsive, 14–17
    emotional, 5
    enjoyment of, 100, 147
    healthy, 27–29
    intuitive approach to, 99–103
    mindfully, 102–3, 185–86

at night, 45, 198

TV watching and, 58, 98, 106, 113

Eating Disorder Foundation of Newfoundland and Labrador, 210

eating disorders, 189–99. *See also* specific disorders

binge eating in, 198

genetic factors in, 159–60

parents and, 141–46

signs of, 4, 199

Eating Disorders Manitoba, 209

Eating Disorder Support Network of Alberta, 208

Eating Disorder Treatment Network, Nova Scotia, 210

Emotion Mind, 82–83

emotions, 6–7, 203

alternative thoughts about, 75–79

effects on reasoning, 74, 82–83

holding on to, 73

managing, 71, 79–87

sharing with others, 129

emulsifiers, 47

endorphins, 114

epicureanism, 5

exaggeration, 74

exercise (physical)

benefits, 114–16, 185

and body image, 139–40

in daily life, 63, 115–16, 173

and hunger cues, 100

obsession with, 127

and sleep, 113

exercises (therapeutic)

changing social models, 126–27

Jacobson's relaxation technique, 79–80

mindful eating, 102–3

mindfulness meditation, 80–81

problem-solving, 85–87

self-compassion, 131–32

self-description (neutral), 137–38

spheres of life, 133–35

visualization, 118–19

Wise Mind, 82–84

F

family dynamics. *See* children; parents

family meals, 141–43

fats (dietary), 47, 64

fibre (dietary), 41, 46

filtering, 73

fish, 46

food. *See also* diet; eating; meals

anxiety-causing, 28, 29, 57, 65, 102–3

children and, 141–43

combining, 64

as comfort, 69–70, 116–17, 130

fermented, 47

glycemic index of, 41, 50, 51, 53–54